Thinking by numbers 4

Written by CAROLINE CLISSOLD

Series editor STEVE HIGGINS

OXFORD
UNIVERSITY PRESS

OXFORD

UNIVERSITY PRESS

Great Clarendon Street, Oxford OX2 6DP

Oxford University Press is a department of the University of Oxford.
It furthers the University's objective of excellence in research,
scholarship, and education by publishing worldwide in

Oxford   New York

Auckland   Cape Town   Dar es Salaam   Hong Kong   Karachi
Kuala Lumpur   Madrid   Melbourne   Mexico City   Nairobi
New Delhi   Shanghai   Taipei   Toronto

With offices in

Argentina   Austria   Brazil   Chile   Czech Republic   France   Greece
Guatemala   Hungary   Italy   Japan   South Korea   Poland   Portugal
Singapore   Switzerland   Thailand   Turkey   Ukraine   Vietnam

Oxford is a registered trade mark of Oxford University Press
in the UK and in certain other countries

Activity text © Caroline Clissold 2005
Introduction text © Steve Higgins 2005

The moral rights of the author have been asserted

Database right Oxford University Press (maker)

First published 2005

British Library Cataloguing in Publication Data

Data available

ISBN-13: 9780198361268
ISBN-10: 019 836126 2

3 5 7 9 10 8 6 4 2

Illustrated by Andrew Keylock
Typeset in Great Britain by Artistix, Thame, Oxon
Printed in Great Britain by Ashford Colour Press, Gosport, Hants

Contents

Introduction

Thinking by Numbers aims to develop thinking skills through mathematics lessons and activities across the primary age range. Although it can be used by an individual teacher, we think that you will get the best from the series if you use the activities across your school to undertake a professional inquiry into the potential of these lessons to develop pupils' thinking. Hence, the sections on *Professional development* (page 9), *Classroom management* (page 12), *Formative assessment and assessment for learning* (page 14), and *Speaking and listening* (page 18) are important aspects of the series. These sections will support you in helping to make the activities successful, as well as suggesting opportunities to develop aspects of your own teaching. Most of these introductory sections also contain suggestions for further reading that will support your exploration of thinking skills through the activities in *Thinking by Numbers*.

Teaching children to think for themselves is at the heart of primary education. It is all too easy to focus on the demands of the curriculum and its assessment and forget that the facts and knowledge have to be connected with an understanding of this curriculum content to help the learner make sense of it all. Without this understanding learners cannot use the information they have been taught and see how it relates to other ideas or knowledge that they have already. At the core of the thinking skills movement in education is the belief that this kind of thinking is teachable. This belief has been inspired by the work of two leading educators.

History of thinking skills

In Israel after the Second World War, many refugee children had been through traumatic early experiences. On traditional tests, such as IQ tests or standardized tests of achievement, many of these children scored so badly that they seemed 'unteachable'. Working to integrate such children Reuven Feuerstein refused to accept this conclusion and devised ways to find out exactly which kinds of thinking they were unable to do, how they could be helped to develop these skills, and, therefore, each individual's *potential* for learning.

Feuerstein developed a set of techniques and tasks called 'instruments' that helped these learners succeed on subsequent tests. These methods were termed 'dynamic', in the sense that children were studying the process of learning and the change that took place. Feuerstein argued that such a process was much more likely to predict how a person might then learn in the future. Many of Feuerstein's ideas have influenced work on teaching thinking skills, in particular his emphasis on the importance of the interaction of the teacher, or 'mediation' of thinking.

Another important figure in thinking skills (or 'Critical Thinking', as it is called in the United States), is the American philosopher Matthew Lipman. As a university professor, he thought that his students had been encouraged to learn facts and to accept opinions, but not to think for themselves. He developed a programme, therefore, called 'Philosophy for Children', which aims to help younger people (from six-year-olds to teenagers) to think by raising questions about stories that they read together. The teacher uses children's natural curiosity about the stories in order to promote active participation and learning. One of Lipman's basic convictions is that children are natural philosophers, and that they view the world around them with curiosity and wonder, which can be used as a basis for thinking and reasoning.

Both Feuerstein and Lipman, though from very different starting-points, hold a similar belief in children's abilities. They have demonstrated that through thinking exercises and activities learners can exceed the predictions of achievement which tests may have suggested is their limit of competence. This, then, forms the basis of techniques in thinking skills – realizing children's potential. Their work has inspired many others to explore and develop approaches which help children to become more effective learners as they start to think for themselves. The aim of this book is to help you, as a teacher, to see how this kind of thinking can be developed.

Teaching thinking

Some people argue that the idea of trying to teach general thinking skills is misguided because in practice thinking always occurs in a specific situation. Further, they believe that it is better to concentrate on teaching subjects and developing specific and detailed knowledge. However, *Thinking by Numbers* has been developed on the principle that there are common features of thinking in different situations, that it is helpful to try to apply techniques learned previously in new situations. For example, once you have used a graphic organizer, such as a Venn diagram, to compare and contrast themes in traditional tales in literacy, you can use the same technique to compare and contrast in other curriculum areas, such as family life in different eras in history.

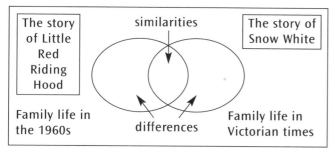

Since 1999, the national curricula for England and Wales now specifically include thinking skills (see page 6 for more details). In Scotland the *5–14 Guidelines* emphasize the capacity for independent thought through enquiry, problem solving, information handling and reasoning, as well as identifying learning and thinking skills in the core skills and capabilities. So the current challenge for teachers is not whether to teach thinking skills, but how best to teach them!

Approaches to teaching thinking skills

There is a host of different programmes and approaches which advocate teaching thinking. These can be categorized broadly into whether they adopt an 'enrichment' approach where they are taught through extra or separate lessons, or an 'infusion' approach where the particular skills are taught through the normal lessons that schools provide. There are certain advantages and disadvantages to adopting these two different teaching approaches. If thinking skills are taught separately it is possible to make skills and techniques explicit, but there is a danger that they may not be used, except in special 'thinking' lessons. However, if they are taught as part of other lessons, such as mathematics or history, there is also a danger that the skills and techniques will become submerged by the curriculum content and not be seen as skills that can be applied elsewhere.

We believe that it is necessary to do both – to have a mixture of 'thinking lessons' with discussion of the kinds of thinking that are involved, and 'subject lessons' where skills can be applied and developed, but perhaps less explicitly. Identifying some lessons as 'thinking maths' lessons gives a clear signal to the children that you are looking for something different in the way that they work and the way they talk and listen. It is challenging to make the time to develop speculation or reasoning in every lesson, but it is also difficult to make sure it happens at *some* time in *some* lessons. We suggest that the activities in the different units can be used as a way to emphasize aspects of thinking that you wish to develop. You may then choose to develop other similar lessons where you can re-use the structure of the activities, or use some of the ideas and techniques in other subject areas.

Suggestions for further reading

H. Sharron and M. Coulter, *Changing Children's Minds: Feuerstein's Revolution in the teaching of Intelligence* (Birmingham, Questions Publishing Company, 1994)

M. Lipman, *Thinking in Education* (Cambridge University Press, 2003)

C. McGuinness, *From thinking skills to thinking classrooms: A review and evaluation of approaches for developing pupils' thinking* [DfEE Research Report RR115] (Norwich, HMSO, 1999)

V. Wilson, *Can Thinking Skills Be Taught? A paper for discussion* (Edinburgh, Scottish Council for Research in Education, 2000) [Available at: http://www.scre.ac.uk/scot-research/thinking/index.html]

Thinking skills and the National Curriculum

Classifying thinking skills

There are more ways to think about thinking than you could imagine! Amongst the wealth of lists, frameworks, models and taxonomies of thinking that have been developed, many people have heard of the 'Bloom's Taxonomy', which is considered the original way of classifying 'higher order thinking'. This taxonomy is basically a three-tier model:

- **knowledge** – in the form of facts, concepts, rules or skills
- **basic thinking** – relatively simple ways of understanding, elaborating and using what is known
- **higher order thinking** – a learning process which leads to a deeper understanding of the nature, justification, implications and value of what is known.

The National Curriculum in England uses five classification headings to denote thinking skills that should be embedded across all subject areas so pupils learn how to learn. These are:

- evaluation
- creativity
- enquiry
- reasoning
- information processing.

However, no single classification or framework can ever fully describe the complexity of all the kinds of thinking we experience. What is missing in both the original version of Bloom's work and in the National Curriculum list is the role of the thinker in thinking – one's own awareness, reflection and engagement. This metacognitive component (i.e. thinking about how we think) is an essential ingredient in developing a learner's understanding of their own thinking and the ability to think for oneself. The following table shows how *Thinking by Numbers* works alongside these thinking classifications to develop thinking skills.

Bloom's Taxonomy	National Curriculum	Thinking by Numbers	
Knowledge Abstracts and universals Using specifics Knowledge of specifics	*Information processing*	Unit 1: Sort it out!	*Unit 6: Think on!*
Basic thinking Application Comprehension			
Higher order thinking Evaluation Synthesis Analysis	*Reasoning* *Enquiry* *Creativity* *Evaluation*	*Unit 2: That's because …* *Unit 3: Detective work* *Unit 4: What if?* *Unit 5: In my opinion*	

Comparison of Bloom's Taxonomy, the National Curriculum and *Thinking by Numbers*

The National Curriculum

The National Curriculum categories contain the following breakdown of skills, which form the basis for the units in the *Thinking by Numbers* series.

Information processing skills

These enable pupils to locate and collect relevant information, to sort, classify, sequence, compare and contrast, and to analyse part/whole relationships.

Reasoning skills

These enable pupils to give reasons for opinions and actions, to draw inferences and make deductions, to use precise language to explain what they think, and to make judgements and decisions informed by reasons or evidence.

Enquiry skills

These enable pupils to ask relevant questions, to pose and define problems, to plan what to do and how to research, to predict outcomes and anticipate consequences, and to test conclusions and improve ideas.

Creative thinking skills

These enable pupils to generate and extend ideas, to suggest hypotheses, to apply imagination, and to look for alternative innovative outcomes.

Evaluation skills

These enable pupils to evaluate information, to judge the value of what they read, hear and do, to develop criteria for judging the value of their own and others' work or ideas, and to have confidence in their judgements.

The first five units of the *Thinking by Numbers* books are based on these classifications. We have also added two further components:

- a final unit which provides opportunities for **using and applying thinking skills** covered in the earlier units
- a **metacognitive skills** element running throughout all of the activities, which aims to develop children's awareness and understanding of the thinking they are doing.

> *Suggestions for further reading*
> L.W. Anderson and D.R. Krathwohl (eds.), *A Taxonomy for Learning, Teaching and Assessing: A revision of Bloom's Taxonomy of Educational Objectives* (New York, Longman, 2001)
>
> S. Higgins, J. Miller, D. Moseley and J. Elliot, 'Taxonomy Heaven', *Teaching Thinking, 12,* (Autumn 2003)

Thinking skills in mathematics

Mathematics is an area of the curriculum which is full of opportunities to develop pupils' thinking skills and reasoning abilities. An emphasis on developing strategies, identifying patterns and rules, and clarifying concepts helps children learn mathematics by making aspects of it more explicit in the classroom. Developing reasoning, problem solving and enquiry skills through mathematics can support the development of these 'higher order' thinking skills more widely, and encourage successful learning in other subjects. A number of principles underpin the activities in each of the six units in *Thinking by Numbers*. These will help pupils to see the connections between the way that they have worked on a mathematics task and then how they can apply these skills in other contexts, either in other areas of mathematics or other areas of learning and understanding.

Challenge

Thinking activities must provide a level of challenge. This means that they should not be too easy to complete, nor so hard that the pupils cannot recognize that they have been successful. Alternatively, the activities may have more than one solution, or route to a solution, that can be evaluated by the pupils to decide which is the best answer or approach. Mathematics is a subject which people often think they just 'can't do'. Successfully completing challenges encourages pupils to see that maths is a subject that they can learn to be good at.

Active discussion

Thinking activities need to be talked about. Mathematics has both a vocabulary and a language of its own. Familiar words are used in unfamiliar ways, such as 'product' or 'difference', and it has its own terminology, such as 'numerator' or 'perpendicular'. Pupils will need time to practise speaking mathematically and explain what they are thinking using this language. This can be difficult to do with the whole class, so some paired or small group work is essential to provide opportunities to explore ideas and allow pupils to develop confidence with the vocabulary.

Feedback

Giving feedback will be key in ensuring pupils make progress in a thinking activity. One of the easiest ways to do this is to have 'mini-plenaries' as the lesson develops. Stop the class for a few minutes and ask a group to explain where they are up to. This will give you the chance to highlight successful ways of working, as well as asking for reasons and challenging their thinking.

Review

When developing thinking skills it is important to review both the **content** of the activity and the **process** that the pupils have used to complete the activity. This means talking about the mathematics involved in the task and the way that they have worked (the skills used in collaborating, working systematically, or identifying patterns and rules). It is often helpful to discuss the latter the next time pupils undertake a similar task so that you can remind them of what was successful. A combination of 'mini-plenaries' throughout the lesson, a review at the end of a lesson, then recapping at the beginning of the next lesson will help ensure children understand that you want them to think not just about *what* they have learned, but *how* they have learned it.

Professional development

We advocate that you try out the *Thinking by Numbers* activities as part of your professional development programme. A critical perspective on the lesson is essential. The activities alone will not succeed in developing thinking skills without this perspective. It is helpful to have a colleague with whom to discuss the activities as you try out the different ideas. We believe that a key part of teaching thinking and thinking skills successfully is to have some time and space to reflect on your own teaching so as to increase the emphasis on developing pupils' understanding. The introductory 'brief' and final 'debrief' sections of each activity aim to support this by summarizing the key features of the lessons and indicating aspects for review.

Thinking by Numbers provides a combination of teacher-led activities, then discussion and collaborative working in small groups, followed by some kind of whole class discussion, or plenary, which reviews both the content and process of learning. The results of this approach are usually a higher level of engagement in the activities, more talking and discussion about the activities. The activities themselves are open-ended to the extent that genuine discussion is not only possible but helpful. They are also challenging but enjoyable activities, helping to create a classroom climate where there is an emphasis on succeeding after effort.

As part of this process you should get more opportunities to hear what your pupils think. As you plan these lessons to increase engagement in learning you will need to listen carefully to how your pupils respond. The enjoyment should initially help to sustain more permanent changes in patterns of classroom interaction. The further feedback you get from insights into pupils' understanding will help identify any misunderstanding or misconceptions that you can tackle through 'mediation' or questioning and discussion.

Some suggestions for getting started:

1 **Work with a colleague**. This might be a colleague teaching the same year group, in which case you can investigate the impact of the same activities. Alternatively you may be working with a colleague in another year group, so you might look at similar kinds of activities or similar aspects of thinking. Working with a colleague means you are more likely to keep to your plan, building progress in time for review. Discussing things with someone else helps to clarify our own thinking, and makes it easier to see patterns or themes in what has happened.

2 **Decide what you want to investigate or improve**. It is easier to develop children's thinking if you focus on a particular area that you feel needs improvement. You could:
   - identify information processing as a key mathematical skill needing improvement
   - focus on your own questioning and how you probe and challenge your children's thinking
   - develop more precise use of mathematical language
   - aim to increase participation in lessons by children who are not usually engaged.

3 **Set a timescale** (at least eight weeks, up to a school year) and plan which activities you are going to use. How often will you have *Thinking by Numbers* lessons? Once a week? Once a fortnight? How will you make sure you have time to review the activities with a colleague?

4 **Try out the activities and review** them as soon afterwards as you can with your colleague. What was different in the lesson compared with other maths lessons? Were you able to see patterns in the children's thinking? Were there any common misconceptions that you needed to tackle? How well did the collaborative tasks go?

5 **Analyse what happened**. If there is improvement, what do you think caused it? The focused practice? Your extra time and effort? The pupils' discussion? Your understanding of their thinking? Would it probably have happened anyway?

6 **Review progress**. What have you learned that you can apply in the longer term? Do some kinds of questions work better than others? Can you use any of the strategies more widely?

How to use *Thinking by Numbers*

The activities in *Thinking by Numbers* can be used in different ways – there is no need to work through them in order, though the final unit is designed to let pupils apply the skills that they have developed. Therefore, for you to assess how well these skills have been learned, it should be used after some of the other activities in the first five units. Some of the activities are based on thinking skills strategies which can be used more widely either in mathematics or other subjects of the curriculum. You should therefore evaluate if there are any aspects of the activity or teaching technique which could be used more generally. Although the books are aimed at different age groups, you may find activities that you can use or adapt in other books in the series. This is particularly true of the generic strategies, such as 'odd one out', which can be used again in mathematics or other areas of the curriculum. See page 24 for a fuller description of some generic activities used throughout the series.

Just as enquiry is at the heart of thinking skills activities for pupils, we believe that it also needs to be a part of the way you use them as a teacher. None of the activities will work by themselves, and they will not all be equally effective since this depends on the existing skills and knowledge of your pupils. You will have to use them critically to see how they can help your pupils' thinking – it is impossible to do this directly, since we cannot see into our pupils' heads and know what they are thinking. Nevertheless, it is possible to plan a series of activities that enable you to find out about pupils' thinking at different times and in different ways. This allows you to infer their level of understanding. Therefore, this needs to be a process of enquiry – finding out what and how your pupils think. The 'Watch out for' and 'Listen for' sections of each activity should help with this process.

The units

The units are based around the classification of thinking skills in the National Curriculum for England and the headings of **information processing**, **reasoning**, **enquiry**, **creative thinking** and **evaluation**. Each unit begins with an overview of these particular aspects of thinking, and ends with a summary looking at how these skills can be developed. Of course, it is not possible to separate the thinking in different activities so that they only involve reasoning or creative thinking. Thinking is a complex activity which involves all kinds of thinking at the same time. It is holistic, multi-dimensional and dependent upon the context that we find ourselves in. The purpose of the tasks in *Thinking by Numbers* is to enable you to focus on a particular kind of thinking and to consider how it can be developed or fostered in your pupils.

Links

The appendices (pages 88 to 95) contain information about how *Thinking by Numbers* relates to the *Framework for Teaching Mathematics* used in England, and the *5–14 Guidelines* for Scotland. A glossary of thinking skills terms is also included on page 96 for reference.

Suggestions for further reading
P. Adey, *The Professional Development of Teachers: Practice and Theory* (Dordrecht, Kluwer Wolters, 2004)

S. Higgins, *Thinking Through Primary Teaching* (Cambridge, Chris Kington Publishing, 2001)

The activities

4 Each activity has a whole class introduction where you will be 'Setting the scene' and modelling the problem to the children.

1 Each activity has an introduction, 'The Brief', and review points, 'The Debrief', to explain the context for the activity. This is the 'professional development' part to help you consider what you want to achieve in the thinking lesson, and later to review how well it achieved its thinking skills aims.

6 The 'Checkpoints' section gives ideas for how to the keep the activity on track. This section also has suggestions on what to watch and listen out for, and prompts and pointers to stimulate discussion.

Who dunnit?

BRIEF

In 'Who dunnit?' the children are asked to find the perpetrator of a crime using the concept of proportion. The activity involves looking at evidence left at a 'crime scene' and using that, along with information that they must work out for themselves, to find the person/s responsible. Enquiry skills are used within the topics of proportion and/or length.

Key maths links
- Using ideas of simple proportion
- Length

Thinking skills
- Enquiry
- Ask relevant questions
- Pose and define problems
- Predict outcomes

Language
proportion, one for every ..., centimetres, circumference, metres, predictions, why?, what could ...?

Resources
- PCM 9 (one per pair)
- PCM 10 (one per pair)
- tape measures
- paper strips (4 cm wide and 45 cm long)
- paper
- pens and pencils

1 Setting the scene

Make up a short story about a robbery, murder or other crime and tell it to the class. It needs to include these facts:
- two things were left at the scene – a hat and a glove
- the length of the glove was 27 cm from tip of middle finger to wrist
- the circumference of the hat was 56 cm
- there were eight suspects, who are pictured on PCM 9 and PCM 10, with their names and their heights.

Explain to the children that they are going to be detectives and try to work out who committed the crime. Say that their only equipment will be themselves, a tape measure, a pair of scissors and strips of paper, plus pen and paper to record their findings.

2 Getting started

Ask: *Do you think this hat and this glove can help us find out who committed the crime? Do you think putting the heights of the people on their pictures is relevant?* Once you have established that all three are probably important, ask the children to work with a partner to try to think why. After a short while ask the children for their thoughts. Aim towards the idea that the distance around their heads and the length of their hands (from tip of middle finger to wrist) are connected to their heights.

Ask the children to work in pairs or small groups to find out how these lengths are connected and what they can do using the tape measure, strips of paper, scissors and themselves to work out a way to solve this problem.

Simplify
Use either the glove or the hat to find one guilty person. Encourage the children to make a strip of paper the same length as their height and one to match their hand measurement, and then see how many times the hand fits into the length. It will be roughly nine times. Discuss how this will help.

Challenge
Ask the children to work out what the lengths of gloves and the circumferences of hats would be if the other people were guilty. Encourage them to make up similar stories with some of the others in the pictures involved.

3 Checkpoints

Stop the class after a short period of time to discuss the initial approaches they have made. If necessary guide the children towards finding connections by asking them to compare the length of their hand (from tip of middle finger to wrist) with their height. Then ask how that might help in this problem. If necessary, repeat for the circumference of their heads and their heights. Ask them to compare findings.

Watch out for ...
Check that the children measure accurately. Circumferences are particularly tricky. Also check out their ability to recognize the connections between the body parts, i.e. three head circumferences are equivalent to one height and nine hand lengths to one height. Are they able to make these connections in order to solve the problem? Some children will benefit from working practically with the strips of paper, so ensure that they have the opportunity to see the relationship (sticking alternating different colours of paper to make a hand length 'ruler' may help).

Ask ...
- *Have you any predictions? What makes you think that?*
- *What ideas have you got to get started?*
- *What is the relationship between the hand and height measurements?*
- *How could you use this relationship to find out who did it?*

Listen for ...
Listen for discussion about how their measurements relate to each other and how this information can be used to solve the problem.

4 Moving on ...

Who solved the problem? Ask one or two of the children to describe to the class how they approached the work and what conclusions they reached. Do the rest of the children agree? Would this evidence stand up in court? What evidence would you need to be convinced of 'who dunnit'?

Where next?
- Is there a proportional relationship between foot size and height?
- Is the relationship more obvious in adults than children?
- What counts as evidence? For a policeman? In history?

DEBRIEF

How often did you intervene? Were your interventions necessary? Would the children benefit from repeating this activity but identifying a different culprit? Did you think it was important to let the children work practically with the strips of paper, or wasn't it necessary for some?

46   47

---

2 Basic information about mathematical objectives and language are included, along with any resources needed, plus the thinking skills focus.

5 The 'Getting started' section shows how the activity can be developed through collaborative group work.

7 Reviewing progress and stimulating further thinking are covered in the 'Moving on' section, as are suggestions to develop the teaching strategy or approach in other mathematics lessons, or in other subjects in 'Where next?'.

3 Each activity has accompanying photocopiable resources. Some are resource sheets for the activities, others aim to support the recording of the activities, particularly by pairs or small groups of pupils (for more information on recording see page 16).

Classroom management

Structure and timing of lessons

Each book in the *Thinking by Numbers* series comprises six units. These are based around the English National Curriculum thinking skills headings of **information processing**, **reasoning**, **enquiry**, **creative thinking** and **evaluation**, with a final unit focused on using and applying the skills acquired through the earlier activities. Each unit contains two activities, with three in the final 'using and applying' unit, giving a total of 13 thinking activities or lessons for each year group. They have been planned as mathematics lessons and cover aspects of the curriculum appropriate for each age group (see the NNS and *Mathematics 5–14* matching charts on pages 90 to 95). You could also use the activities as thinking lessons and follow the suggestions at the end of each unit to develop the ideas and thinking strategies across the curriculum. When planning how to use the activities there are a number of different approaches you could take, and these are outlined here.

Regular thinking skills development

You could work through the activities using a *Thinking by Numbers* activity every two or three weeks. The benefit of this approach is that it provides regular opportunities to highlight the thinking skills you want to develop across the year. In the intervening time you would need to make sure that you refer back to the lessons and activities, as it would be all too easy for your pupils, particularly younger children, to forget what you are looking for in their work in the thinking activities.

Intensive thinking skills development

You could choose to work through the units more intensively, perhaps one activity each week over a term, so that you could then take the skills and ideas further over the course of the year. This may also be more suitable for year groups in England where your teaching is affected by statutory tests, such as Year 6 in particular. A further advantage of this approach is that you can build up some momentum with regular 'thinking maths' lessons. Assuming they go well initially, the children will start to look forward to the lessons and you can then capitalize on this enthusiasm. You will also

develop a language around the lessons and activities with your class, and the regular practice will enhance this development.

Integrated thinking skills development

Another possible approach for teachers in England and Scotland is to use the matching charts to the *NNS Framework* or *Mathematics 5–14*. These are provided in the appendices and will enable you to substitute the *Thinking by Numbers* activities where they fit most appropriately in your usual teaching plan. Whilst this is less disruptive to the mathematics curriculum, you will need to work hard to develop the thinking themes in the book. The thinking skills issue here is how you get the children to use what they learn elsewhere. This is always a challenge with any learning at school: how do you get learners to transfer what they know or can do to a new situation? The concept of 'bridging' is a useful one. As a teacher you connect or 'bridge' the knowledge or skills between different contexts. Where you have regular lessons you can mention things that you then refer to in other lessons. The further apart the sessions, the harder you will have to work to make those connections meaningful. *You remember when we used a Venn diagram to look at similarities and differences? Could we do something similar here?*

Managing the lesson

To use the *Thinking by Numbers* activities effectively you will need to think through the method of working. Your pupils will need to have a clear idea of what they are doing, and why, so that in the review sections of the lesson they can evaluate how successful they have been. It is important to get the lessons off to a good start, so the children will need a 'hook' or some initial stimulus to launch into the activity well. This can be either through the way you introduce the activity, the resources that are used, or perhaps the way you make it meaningful to the pupils, tapping into their particular interests or enthusiasms. It is hard to predict exactly how long the different activities will take to complete. Sometimes children become particularly enthusiastic about a particular task and you will struggle to get through everything that is suggested. On other occasions you will have time to review the activities and ask the children to reflect on their learning.

Introducing the lesson

Each activity begins with some kind of whole class introduction or demonstration. In this part of the lesson it is important to explain the activity and its purpose clearly. You should make objectives explicit; explain what you want from the pupils in terms of how they should work and the kind of language they should use. You will need to get feedback from the pupils to evaluate whether they understand what they are doing and know what they will have to do in the next phase of the activity. You may also need to adapt the activities according to the needs of your pupils. Although the activities have been designed for particular ages of pupils, you will need to judge whether some alteration is needed to provide the appropriate level of challenge for your class.

During the lesson

In most of the activities the pupils apply or extend the ideas presented in the introduction by working collaboratively in pairs or small groups. When moving from whole-class to paired or group work, it is useful to discuss or mention how the pairs or groups are going to work together and what you are looking for. At the transition it is worth praising specific behaviours: *I liked the way you sorted out the number cards for your group, David.* Though it is also important to tailor this praise, particularly for older pupils who should be aware of supportive behaviours and active listening strategies: *Your group got started really quickly, Emma, what was it that you each did?* Reinforce the method of sharing ideas, explaining that they can do better together than they can separately, and that copying and ownership of ideas are not factors. The tasks themselves are designed to be challenging and to benefit from some discussion in small groups so that pupils don't just make up their minds quickly. The activities also contain suggestions for differentiation, with advice on simplifications and challenges that should help you to ensure that the level of challenge is maintained as the pupils work through the tasks. Further advice on

the opportunities to develop speaking and listening skills are outlined on pages 18 and 19.

Reviewing the lesson

The hardest part of these activities is in helping pupils to see that particular tactics, strategies or approaches are helpful, without teaching specific solutions or answers. This will require some skilful questioning and discussion. It is important to review both the process that the pupils have used, particularly the collaborative skills of speaking and listening, as well as reviewing the curriculum content and knowledge and understanding of the activities.

It is also a good idea to review some of this as the lesson unfolds, rather than waiting until the end. Whilst the plenary seems to be the logical place to review the lesson, the pupils also know that the lesson is drawing to an end and it can be hard to maintain their interest. Mini-plenaries are, therefore, an essential teaching strategy which can help make the activities successful. These can be very brief, just checking where groups are up to, or sharing a successful technique or tactic being used by some children. *I noticed you've sorted the cards into different groups, can you tell the class how they are organized?* It boosts their confidence if you draw this to the attention of the whole class and gives other pupils who may not be on track a clear hint about what they could do.

Another possibility is to recap at the beginning of the next lesson. This is essential if the *Thinking by Numbers* sessions are a week or more apart. You need to remind the children that these are different lessons which require thinking, explaining, reasoning and evaluating. There should be more time for discussion about what went well previously and what skills or strategies they might find useful. The main aim is to help the pupils understand that they might not be able to see a solution immediately, but by thinking and working together they will be able to complete the activity successfully. In mathematics this is particularly important as it is a subject which pupils tend to think that they are either good at or not good at, rather than a subject that they can all learn to be better at!

Formative assessment and assessment for learning

Formative assessment is about intervening during teaching to improve learning. As a teacher you gather feedback about what is going on (either within a lesson or between lessons) and use that information to alter what you do subsequently. Assessment for learning is a more interactive approach that takes assessment a stage further by involving the learners in understanding what the specific learning objectives are for each activity/task/lesson so that they can judge how successful they have been in achieving them. This helps teachers and pupils to understand the criteria for being successful at learning, both for short term objectives as well as longer term goals about 'learning to learn' more effectively.

When assessing for learning it is important to give pupils feedback about what they can do to improve (rather than giving marks or feedback that simply indicates whether they are correct or not). One common technique is to get pupils to give you feedback about how well they think they are doing on an activity or a piece of work. This can be a simple thumbs up/down signal from the class, or getting pupils to use traffic light colours to self-assess a piece of work they have done – green for go ('I understand it and can go on'), orange for getting there ('I could do with a little bit of help'), red for stop ('I'm stuck').

Thinking skills approaches also involve formative assessment. Most of the activities are about giving you, the teacher, information about children's thinking. This lets you assess their understanding and make decisions about how to support the development of that thinking. In addition, pupils are expected to talk about their thinking as they undertake the tasks. Developing this metacognitive talk (talk about their own thinking) is a powerful technique which helps learners understand their learning better.

Furthermore, focusing on what makes for successful learning encourages judgement about that learning and moves the discussion away from the products

or outputs (such as a complete page of calculations) to what has been learned (such as, 'I am finding subtraction more difficult than addition'). The concept of transfer is crucial here since it moves learning away from the particular to the more general. *What have you learned today that you can use in the future? What have you learned previously that will help you now?*

Both assessment for learning and thinking skills approaches use collaborative techniques for learning: paired and group work so that learners benefit from discussion with their peers. Both approaches highlight the role of the teacher in effective questioning and discussions with the pupils to move their thinking on. Assessment for learning and thinking skills approaches are clearly complementary. If you are developing formative assessment you will be developing children's thinking skills. If you are developing children's thinking skills and being explicit about the thinking they are doing with them, then this is formative assessment!

Suggestions for further reading

Primary National Strategy, *Excellence and Enjoyment: learning and teaching in the primary years. Planning and assessment for learning: assessment for learning* (Document code: DfES 0521-2004 G) (2004)

Assessment Reform Group, *Assessment for Learning: 10 principles* (London, QCA, 2002) (available online at: http://www.qca.org.uk/ages3-14/downloads/afl_principles.pdf)

P. Black, C. Harrison, C. Lee, B. Marshall and D. William, *Assessment for Learning. Putting it into practice.* (Maidenhead, Open University Press, 2003)

S. Clarke, *Unlocking Formative Assessment: Practical strategies for enhancing pupils' learning in the primary classroom* (London, Hodder and Stoughton, 2001)

How do you know it is working?

One of the greatest challenges in developing learners' thinking is assessing how well the activities are going. You should feel that the tasks and activities are giving the children opportunities to think and you should get direct and indirect evidence of this. There are a number of ways that you can start to gauge the impact of the activities.

Enjoyment

First and foremost the activities should be enjoyable, both for you and your class. It is important that the activities are regarded as fun because this helps the children to develop their confidence to discuss what they think. It encourages the children to offer opinions and ideas without the worry of being 'wrong'. This aspect of the activities is vital to ensure their success. Thinking is hard work, so it needs to be as enjoyable as possible!

Participation

Enjoyment should lead to increased engagement and involvement in the lessons. One of the ways that you can assess this is by keeping track of who participates. Are the contributions coming from those who are usually involved and usually speak in whole class discussions? Can you use the paired or group work to build pupils' confidence in contributing to a whole class discussion? *I thought that your suggestion was a really good one – can you explain it to the class?* Are you getting spontaneous contributions from those you normally have to ask directly?

Language

The next thing to watch for is language that indicates thinking and reasoning. Are the pupils giving reasons? Do they use words like *then, so, because*? Are they being tentative (*I think … It could be … It might be …*) or speculative (*What if …? How about if we …?*)? You can start the lesson by saying you want to hear particular phrases, and giving suggestions for how they may be used. Then you need to look out for these first when the children are working in pairs or small groups. Then encourage the children to give longer responses in class discussions, ask them for reasons or examples, or to comment on each other's ideas. One of the most effective ways of encouraging this is simply to wait longer when you ask a question, and wait a little bit longer at the end of the response whilst indicating that you want them to continue. In mathematics you should also see the children using specific vocabulary more precisely; for example, are they getting more accurate in the use of words like *number, numeral* and *digit*? Or terms like *side, corner, edge* and *vertex*? You should also pay attention to the questions that the children ask. If the lessons are successful, the children will be asking questions about the content of the learning (rather than just about what they have to do).

Reflection

If the activities are working the children should know that they have been successful and that they have been thinking hard. They should show growing awareness of this and be able to talk about their thinking. At first this will come out during the activities or just as you finish. It is a good tactic to get them to review and reflect at the beginning of the next *Thinking by Numbers* task; this will help remind them of what is expected in the next task as well as giving you a chance to assess how much they recall from last time!

Transfer

The long term goal of *Thinking by Numbers* is to develop transferable skills. Evidence of this is shown when children start to refer back to thinking skills activities in terms of what they have learned. You should, therefore, begin to notice that they are using and talking about the skills that they are developing in other maths lessons or in other subjects. If this is spontaneous or unprompted you know that they are using the thinking skills for themselves.

Recording

Opportunities for recording are identified in most of the activities. However, there are a number of issues you will need to consider. The activities are about developing thinking and the lesson must focus on this as the most important outcome. Recording can distract from this if the children become concerned with making sure they 'get it right' when they have to write something down. There are two main aspects of recording. The first is the recording of the particular task. Some of the photocopiable resources are explicitly designed for this. For other activities the children will need to think about the best way to record their thinking and their progress through the activity. The activities are often collaborative so you may need to make copies of the completed sheet for all the children in the group.

The second aspect of recording is to support review of the activities. The 'What did you learn today?' photocopiable sheet (see page 17) is designed to help with this. It may not be appropriate to use it for every activity, but it will help you review aspects of the lesson that enable the children to develop an understanding of their thinking and their learning (see *Formative assessment and assessment for learning* on page 14 for more information about developing thinking about learning). This aspect is cumulative and progressive as you will need to encourage the children to think about:

- their learning
- what they did
- what kind of thinking was involved
- how they worked together
- what lessons or skills they have learned that they can use in the future.

When planning how to incorporate recording into a thinking lesson, it is helpful to consider the following principles.

1   Recording should be purposeful
The record should either help with the process of the task or capture aspects of the thinking that it will be helpful to review.

2   Recording should be integral
If keeping track of what they are doing is not part of the task, it becomes an extra burden and less likely to be completed effectively.

3   Recording should be used
If you ask the children to make some notes on their thinking, or to use the 'What did you learn today?' PCM, you need to make use of it in a discussion either in that lesson or as part of setting the scene for the next activity.

4   Recording should be short
The lessons are about thinking and this needs to be the most important part of the lesson. You will not be able to capture everything that happens; you may need to have some kind of record to keep track of what has happened, but keep it as simple as possible.

What did you learn today?

Name _____ Date _____

What did you learn today? _____
_____
_____

What kind of thinking did you do today?

	Yes	No
I remembered things that were useful	☐	☐
I organized my ideas	☐	☐
I thought of reasons	☐	☐
I found out something I did not know	☐	☐
I used a rule or a pattern to work something out	☐	☐
I had a new idea	☐	☐
I was methodical	☐	☐

How challenging was it?

Circle one of the choices on the line.

Very easy   Easy   OK   Hard   Very hard

Working with others

	Yes	No
I asked my teacher a question	☐	☐
I asked my partner a question	☐	☐
I asked a question in my group	☐	☐
I shared my ideas	☐	☐
I changed my mind	☐	☐
I was good at listening to my partner	☐	☐

Speaking and listening

Talking, thinking and learning are all closely related. We can remember things that we have heard, but it is only when we can put these ideas into our own words that we know we have learned them effectively. Speaking and listening are, therefore, at the heart of any thinking skills work. Listening to your pupils talk is also the best feedback you can get to assess what they are actually learning. It is therefore essential that the lessons and activities have speaking and listening at their core.

Children should be able to explain not just what they are doing, but why, and that their thinking is about the learning they are involved in. This involves speaking, listening and participating effectively in small and large group discussions. This helps them to learn by using new vocabulary (or words they already know more accurately) to express new ideas and new thinking. This process is difficult and requires time and support. Part of the purpose of the group work is to allow this to happen. Children will hear their peers making suggestions and having ideas about the tasks. As they join in and make their own suggestions they will work together to find a solution. This will help children succeed more independently in future tasks. The discussions with the whole class will help them to be more confident in what they are saying and thinking, and will give you opportunities to provide feedback on what you are looking for in thinking lessons. The table on page 19 sets out a progression in speaking, listening and group discussion and interaction across the primary age range.

Classroom language

Classroom language is like a dialect of English. It has particular features and implicit rules that are different from language outside of school. The way you take turns, as a pupil, is very different from the way you normally take turns in conversation, either with your friends or at home. The teacher's use of questions, in particular, is strikingly different. Questions are often heavily loaded. For example, if you ask 'Why did you write that?', a child may assume that you are challenging them because it is incorrect and that they should have put something else. In a thinking skills lesson you may be wanting them to explain the reasons for their choices, or the decisions they made about what to write down, so as to provide a model for the rest of the class. If a teacher asks 'What do you *think* you should do?', the pupils may assume that you are reprimanding them for not listening, rather than asking them to speculate. It is therefore very important to think carefully about the questions that you ask to try to ensure that your pupils understand you really *do* want to know what they are thinking! Some examples of good questions are provided on page 21.

Talking maths

Mathematical language is also different from everyday English. It is important that children do not just learn and remember the vocabulary, but learn how to use the language to communicate. This will help them to develop their mathematical thinking. Many words have specialist meanings in maths lessons, such as 'odd' and 'even'. Other words may not be encountered outside of these lessons, for example, 'trapezium' and 'numerator'. The *Thinking by Numbers* activities are a chance for children to speak the language of mathematics, rather than just practise its vocabulary.

Suggestions for further reading
Primary National Strategy, *Speaking, Listening, Learning: Working with children in Key Stages 1 and 2. Professional development materials* (Document code: DfES 0163-2004) (2004)

N. Mercer, *Words and Minds: How We Use Language To Think Together* (London, Routledge, 2000)

S. Higgins, *Parlez-vous mathematics? Enhancing Primary Mathematics Teaching and Learning*, I. Thompson (ed.) (Buckingham, Open University Press, 2003)

A skills progression in ...

	... Speaking	... Listening	... Group discussion and interaction
Y1/2	▶ Speak clearly and expressively in supportive contexts on a familiar topic. ▶ Order talk reasonably and pace well when recounting events or actions. ▶ Talk engagingly to listeners with emphasis and varied intonation. ▶ Able to use gestures and visual aids to highlight meanings.	▶ Listen actively following practical consequences, e.g.: – looking at a speaker – asking for repetition if needed. ▶ Able to clarify and retain information: – by acting on instructions – by rephrasing in collaboration with others – by asking for more specific information.	▶ Talk purposefully in pairs and small groups. ▶ Contribute ideas in plenary and whole-class discussions. ▶ Make and share predictions, take turns, contribute to review of group discussion. ▶ Review and comment on effectiveness of group discussions.
Y3/4	▶ Sustain speaking to a range of listeners, explaining reasons, or why something interests them. ▶ Organize and structure subject matter of their own choice, and pace their talk (including pauses for interaction with listeners) for emphasis and meaning. ▶ Adapt talk to the needs of the listeners (such as to visitors or more formal contexts), showing awareness of standard English.	▶ Sustain listening independently and make notes about what different speakers say, identifying the gist, key ideas and links between them. ▶ Able to comment and respond, evaluating a speaker's contribution, or evaluate quality of information provided. ▶ Able to concentrate in different contexts, including talk without/by actions and visual aids.	▶ Sustain different roles in group work (with support from a teacher), including leading and summarizing main reasons for a decision. ▶ Talk about language needed to carry out such roles and how they contribute to the overall effectiveness of the work. ▶ Reflect constructively on strengths and weaknesses of group talk.
Y5/6	▶ Develop ideas in extended turns for a range of purposes. ▶ Assimilate information from different sources and contrasting points of view, present ideas in ways appropriate to spoken language. ▶ Use features of standard English appropriately in more formal contexts. ▶ Make connections and organize thinking.	▶ Listen actively and selectively for content and tone. ▶ Able to distinguish different registers, moving between formal and informal language according to the audience, and emphasize or undercut surface meanings. ▶ Able to discern different threads in an argument or the nuances in talk.	▶ Organize and manage collaborative tasks over time and in different contexts with minimal supervision. ▶ Negotiate disagreements and possible solutions, by clarifying the extent of differences, or by putting ideas to the vote. ▶ Vary the register and precision of their language and comment on the choices made in more formal contexts.

Adapted from Primary National Strategy, *Speaking, Listening, Learning: Working with children in Key Stages 1 and 2 Handbook* (Norwich, DfES/HMSO, 2003)

Collaborative group work

Collaborative group work is an essential part of thinking skills teaching. The opportunity to work with a partner or in a small group is essential. This is where children can explore their own thinking, hear other people's ideas, be tentative, make mistakes, but be supported and encouraged by their peers. This is how an individual develops confidence in new ways of thinking. However, it does not happen automatically. You will need to make time for it, support, nurture and encourage it.

Plan for it

Thinking about who is going to work with whom, and how, is essential. It won't just happen until the class are used to this way of working, and even then there will be new skills they can develop. Most thinking skills lessons are based on mixed groups that are not based on current levels of attainment. However, you will need to monitor who works well with whom and support the children in working with a wider range of their peers.

Make it explicit

The children need to know that they are expected to work together, and that you are expecting them to help each other. This needs continual reinforcement with the whole class in the introduction, mini-plenaries and review sections of lessons (praising and reminding groups and individuals helps, too).

Teach pupils how to work in groups

Not all children find it easy to cooperate. They may well need the first few activities to focus on learning to work together. It is worth making this a part of your learning objectives for speaking and listening (see pages 18 to 19). In one of the early sessions (if you have not done so already), it is worth agreeing class rules for working in groups or a 'working together protocol'. Such an agreement should be phrased positively about what children should do and might include things like:

- Make sure everybody has a turn in speaking
- One person speaks at a time
- Look at the person who is talking (make eye contact)
- Listen actively (positive body language such as nodding or an open posture)
- Speak clearly
- Explain what you mean
- Respond to what other people say
- Make a longer contribution than just one or two words
- Give reasons for what you think
- Make it clear when you disagree that it is with what has been said (with your reasons) and not a person.

However, it is important that the precise wording comes from the children and that the agreement is posted publicly where it will always be visible in the classroom. The children will use it!

Start small

Pairs are the easiest groups to start with. In Key Stage 1 this should be the main aim. Even very young children should be able to cooperate in pairs, particularly if the cooperation is structured in some way (such as taking turns in a game). Moving from pairs to fours is a good tactic too. A paired task can be reviewed by two pairs to reach agreement, then this larger grouping can form the basis for a further activity.

Make sure the tasks require cooperation

Consider strategies such as having one recording sheet, or set of resources that need to be shared, or assign specific tasks to each member of the group. As groups get bigger you may need to assign different roles and let the children practise the different skills required (for example, leader, note taker, summarizer, clarifier). In the beginning it is best to use existing friendships as the basis for organizing the groups, but don't let them get too cosy. Learning to work with people who are not close friends is an important skill for life!

> ### *Suggestions for further reading*
> L. Dawes, N. Mercer and R. Wegerif, *Thinking Together: Activities for teachers and children at Key Stage 2* (Birmingham, Questions Publishing Co., 2000)

Talking points

Getting started

How are you going to tackle this?
What information have you got to help you?
What do you need to find out or do?
How are you going to do it? Why that way?
Can you think of any questions you will need to ask?
What do you think the answer will look like?
Can you make a prediction?

Supporting progress

Can you explain what you have done so far?
What else do you need to do?
Can you think of another way that might have worked?
What do you mean by ...?
What did you notice when ...?
Are you beginning to see a pattern or a rule?

If someone is stuck ...

Can you say what you have to do in your own words?
Can you talk me through where you are up to?
Is there something that you know already that might help you?
How could you sort things out to help you?
Would a picture help, or a table/sketch/diagram/graph?
Have you talked with your partner/another pair/group about what they are doing?

Reviewing learning

What have you learned today?
What would you do differently if you were doing this again?
When could you use this approach/idea again?
What are the key points or ideas that you need to remember?
Did it work out the way you expected?
How did you check it?

Remember – one way to ask a question is just to wait!

Suggestions for further reading
Association of Teachers of Mathematics, *Primary Questions and Prompts* (Derby, ATM, 2004)

Thinking skills across the curriculum

There are a number of general teaching strategies that you can explore to support the activities in *Thinking by Numbers*. They are helpful because you can use the same technique in different contexts and develop thinking across the curriculum. Each time you use these strategies you can focus on the children's thinking that you want to develop. The children become familiar with the techniques and can get straight down to the learning involved. The strategies are also useful in assessing the children's understanding. If you first **demonstrate** a technique or approach, you can then set an activity which the children **undertake** to develop their thinking. This is as far as most approaches to thinking skills go. However, if you then set a challenge where the children have to **generate** their own activity based on what they have done, you will see them reveal their understanding of the thinking required. This cycle of **demonstrate**, **undertake** and **generate** ensures that the thinking becomes embedded.

Odd one out

In this strategy the children are presented with three items and asked to choose one as the 'odd one out' and to give a reason. Items are chosen to ensure that a range of answers is possible. Pupils can also be asked to identify the similar corresponding characteristic of the other two, or features common to all, to develop their vocabulary and understanding. In mathematics this leads naturally on to a discussion of the properties of numbers and to identifying numbers which have a range of properties. It can easily be extended to work on shapes or into other subjects. Selecting three items with different possible reasons is essential. When the children design their own game, it is essential that you emphasize that there should be more than one solution or 'answer'. It leads on to identifying common properties that the odd one out lacks.

9, 5 and 10 – which is the odd one out and why?

9 because it's a square number … 10 because it has 2 digits or because it is even… 5 because it is prime…

Living graphs

The strategy involves a graph or a chart as the basis for an activity where the children have to relate short statements to the more abstract structure of a graph. The use of statements that children can understand easily, but which they then have to discuss and interpret, helps them to make sense of both the representation of the graph and the information it is based on. This works well in mathematics and science, but also in other subjects where quantitative information is used, such as history and geography.

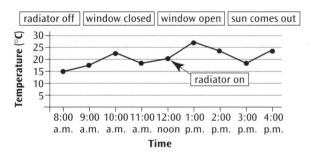

Sorting strategies

Venn diagrams, Carroll diagrams, grids and matrices are effective strategies to display information visually. They support skills such as collecting, sorting, classifying and organizing ideas and information across the curriculum. Sorting techniques are powerful because they provide examples of what a concept or idea is and importantly what it is *not*.

Always, sometimes, never

Another useful strategy is to have a set of statements, such as 'triangles have three sides' or 'multiples of 3 are odd' and ask the children if they are 'always' true, 'sometimes' true or 'never' true. This works well in mathematics and science: in other subjects you may need to set these categories along a continuum to provoke discussion.

As before, asking the children to make up statements that are always, sometimes or never true is a good way to extend the task (and their thinking).

Fermi questions

The approach of Enrico Fermi, who was an Italian scientist who used to pose questions to get his team thinking and working together, works well in the classroom. At school a question such as: *How many balloons would it take to fill the school hall?* requires the children to ask a number of related questions along the lies of, *How big is a balloon? How big is the hall?* This particularly develops estimation and approximation skills. Discussion and reasoning is an important part of the process of answering them. Other questions might be: *How many chocolate beans will it take to fill a litre lemonade bottle? What is the total mass of all the children in the school?* Or *If everyone in school (or the class) lay down in a line from the school gate (or classroom door), head to toe, where would the line end?* Once the children get used to answering questions like this you can ask them to think up their own.

Mysteries

In this strategy children are given information that they use to answer a central question. They work in pairs or small groups to look through short statements on little pieces of paper or card. Then they have to draw inferences and make links between the pieces of information in order to answer the question. The statements contain enough information to require the children to make inferences or identify misleading 'clues'. A mystery can be mathematical (see Year 6 'Birdwatching' page 70), or designed to support evaluation in other subjects such as history or geography.

Why do we remember Guy Fawkes?	
James the First was king of England between 1603 and 1625	Some people wanted to get rid of the king
Some of Guy Fawkes' friends were very angry with the king because of the way he ran the church	When Guy Fawkes was executed people celebrated by lighting bonfires
The king opened Parliament on the afternoon of November 5th 1605	Lots of Guy Fawkes' friends were also arrested. They were all sentenced to death
Guy Fawkes was found in the cellar underneath the Houses of Parliament with 36 barrels of gunpowder	Guy Fawkes was arrested very early in the morning of November 5th 1605

PMI

PMI stands for 'Plus/Minus/Interesting' and is a technique developed by Edward de Bono (as part of his Cognitive Research Trust [CoRT] programme) to get beyond the basic 'pros and cons' approach and the snap decisions that can result from this. When there is a difficult decision or where evaluation is needed, draw up a table headed up 'Plus', 'Minus', and 'Interesting'. In the column underneath the 'Plus' heading, ask the children to write down all the positive points of taking the action. Underneath the 'Minus' heading they write down all the negative points. In the 'Interesting' column they write any further thoughts that strike them. These can be scored across the class to find out how many plus and minus points there are as a method of voting.

Think/Pair/Share

This is a good general technique to get everyone thinking. Instead of getting a response from an individual pupil, ask the whole class to work out the answer, then see if the person next to them agrees, then ask each pair to discuss what they have agreed with another pair. A further variation gets the children to record their thinking before discussing it with a partner: 'Think/Ink/Pair/Share'.

Activities in this book

Unit 1 Sort it out! *Information processing skills*	**Aliens ahoy! (p 26–29)** Children are presented with 'aliens' that have different numbers of arms and asked to find out how many of each creature there could be for a given number of arms, then to explain why using their knowledge of multiples and factors. **Need to know (p 30–33)** The children are asked to work out how much items from a selection of shops cost and use a series of clues to work out how to solve the problem.
Unit 2 That's because … *Reasoning skills*	**I can, I can't (p 36–39)** The children use a set of statements and eight shapes to make an 'I can' statement about the shapes to develop their reasoning about the properties of polygons. **Up the mountain (p 40–43)** The children work their way up a mountain path by finding links between adjacent numbers. They then make up their own 'path' identifying as many links as they can.
Unit 3 Detective work *Enquiry skills*	**Who dunnit? (p 46–49)** The children find the perpetrator of a crime using the concept of proportion to make inferences about a likely culprit. **Mystery numbers (p 50–53)** The children plan how to identify the possible missing numbers to complete a number grid and formulate a rule for generating all the possibilities.
Unit 4 What if …? *Creative thinking skills*	**Tell me a story (p 56–59)** The children generate digital clock times using digit cards, order the times and then create stories using these times. **Fraction time! (p 60–63)** An analogue clock is used to make fractions and then investigate different equivalent fractions that can be created from these.
Unit 5 In my opinion … *Evaluation skills*	**Good buy? (p 66–69)** The children design an outfit with accessories to fit certain criteria, one of which is a financial constraint. This encourages the children to evaluate information and make decisions. **Best fit (70–73)** The children sort numbers into a Venn diagram according to given criteria and use their knowledge of multiplication and division to evaluate and justify their choices.
Unit 6 Think on! *Using and applying thinking skills*	**Sweetie dilemma (p 76–79)** Children use and apply their mathematical knowledge to solve a problem based on a graph to provide opportunities to assess aspects of their thinking. **Money, money, money! (p 80–83)** The children apply their problem solving skills to identify relevant information and decide on a system to find all possible solutions about paying for items with different coins. **What's my angle? (p 84–87)** The children apply their knowledge of angles to develop understanding of other shapes in a problem-solving task.

Sort it out!

Information processing skills

> **Information processing** – these skills enable pupils to locate and collect relevant information, to sort, classify, sequence, compare, contrast and analyze part/whole relationships. (QCA 2000)

Overview

This unit is about working with mathematical ideas and concepts by gathering information. It is about building understanding by actively working with these concepts and ideas. It is about remembering links and making connections to understand what information is relevant. It is also about working with ideas to develop understanding of their meaning by working with patterns and rules, working with definitions and organizing and representing ideas. It is an essential aspect of mathematical thinking. The activities in this unit are designed to help pupils engage practically with ideas and information so as to build their knowledge and understanding of mathematical concepts.

Strategies

Information processing skills can be broken down further into the following kinds of behaviours or activities that pupils can do:

- **Find relevant information**
  Remember, recall, search, recognize, identify
- **Collect relevant information**
  Retrieve, identify, select, gather, choose
- **Sort**
  Group, include, exclude, list, make a collection or set
- **Classify**
  Sort, order, arrange *by kind or type*
- **Sequence**
  Order, arrange *by quantity/size/weight*, put in an array
- **Compare**
  Find similarities/differences, examine, relate, liken
- **Contrast**
  Find differences (and similarities), examine, distinguish
- **Analyze part/whole relationships**
  Relate, consider, sort out, make links *between parts and wholes* (e.g. component/integral object (such as the face of a cube); member/collection; portion/mass; stuff/object; place/area; feature/activity; especially in terms of fractions, ratios and the like).

Questions

Can you think of something that might help? What does this remind you of?
Give me an example of a ... Is ... an example? Can you give a counter-example?
What would come next? What would come before this?
Why is it the same/different? What makes it a ...? What is it like? What makes a ... different from a ...?

Aliens ahoy!

BRIEF

In 'Aliens ahoy' the children are presented with 'aliens' that have different numbers of arms. They are asked to find out how many of each creature there could be for a given number of arms and to explain why. They are encouraged to sort numbers into multiples, chunk numbers that are composed of lots of factors, look at the relationship between odd and even numbers and make judgements using mathematical knowledge in order to obtain a solution. It gives you the opportunity to hear their reasoning and thinking as they justify their ideas, and also to assess their confidence with multiples and properties of odd and even numbers.

Key maths links

- Properties of numbers
- Reasoning about numbers

Thinking skills

- Sorting
- Classifying
- Comparing

Language

odd, even, multiple, pairs, because, so, I think this

Resources

PCM 1 (one per group and one enlarged)

pens or pencils

PCM 2 (one per pair/group)

① Setting the scene

Show an enlarged version of PCM 1 about Planet Legless. Read the problem. *What might help us to solve this problem? Which of our times table may help? Why? Do you think knowing about odd and even numbers may be useful?* Recap addition of odd and even numbers, discuss how this information helps.

② Getting started

Ask the children to work in pairs to find a solution. Bring the class together when one is found, ask for an explanation. Then ask for all other possibilities.

What did we need to do to solve this problem? Look for:

- List of multiples of 2 and 3.
- Use odd multiple of 3 and multiple of 2 totalling 27. 9
- Find all possible answers.

Discuss the idea of 'chunking' numbers into multiples of 2 and 3, e.g. 29 into 20 and 9 (giving 10 Bimen and 3 Trimen), 10 and 18 (giving 5 Bimen and 6 Trimen). The children could make a table of the multiples of 2 and 3 to look for all of the possible combinations.

Try another problem: *There are Trimen and Quadmen instead of Bimen. 31 arms can be seen, how many of each alien might there be? Find all the possibilities.* When completed, give an even number of arms, e.g. 38. Ask: *How can our knowledge of odd and even numbers help us?*

+	3	6	9	12	15
2	5	8	11	14	17
4	7	10	13	16	19
6	9	12	15	18	21
8	11	14	17	20	23
10	13	16	19	22	25
12	15	18	21	24	27
14	17	20	23	26	29
16	19	22	25	28	31
18	21	24	27	30	33
20	23	26	29	32	35

Multiples of 2 and 3

Simplify

Keep working with Bimen and Trimen. It may be helpful to give the children cut-outs of the aliens, so they can count the arms. Give different numbers of arms, e.g. 23, 20. You may need to help them organize their work.

Challenge

After the children have completed the first problem, give them others, e.g. *There are Bimen, Quadmen and Quinmen and 34 arms. How many of each might there be?*

Checkpoints

Monitor the activity by sitting with groups of children and observing what they are doing, helping only if necessary. Check that they are talking to each other. Every so often, call the class or groups working on the same task together and ask them to feedback what they have done so far.

Continue on the second part of the task. Ask if they noticed something different about the outcome in terms of odd and even numbers.

Watch out for ...

Look for children who are working well together. Those showing sensible, systematic recording, intervene and direct those who aren't. Are the children confident in their knowledge of multiples and properties of odd and even numbers? If not, again give guidance. Can they 'chunk' numbers into multiples? Can they use a grid structure efficiently? (such as by using what they know to rule out some combinations)

Ask ...

- *Could we have used an even number of Trimen? (no) Why not? (the total number of arms is odd, all Bimen are even and if you add an even number of Trimen you will get an even number of arms)*
- *How are you recording your work?*
- *Have you found all the solutions? How do you know?*
- *What in particular helped you to come to a solution?*

Listen for ...

Observe the children as they talk to each other. Listen for the use of appropriate vocabulary, e.g. multiples, I think this because. Listen for explanations as to why certain combinations work and others don't, e.g. Those two numbers won't work because we need to find two even numbers to add and that one is odd.

 Moving on ...

Review the solutions the children found. Did they find all possibilities? How do they know that? Ask what they did that helped them get to the solutions, e.g. did they use the rules of addition of odd and even numbers?

Invite a few children to share the problems they made up with the class.

Where next?

- Try the same type of activity but use 3 to 8 sided polygons.
- Try the same type of activity but involving money, e.g. *I have some 10p, 5p and 2p coins. I have a total of 23p. What combinations of coins could I have?*

What worked well? Was it challenging enough? Did you give enough structured support when it was needed? Are there areas of mathematical knowledge that need revisiting? Did any of the children surprise you? Did the visual support of the grid help?

DEBRIEF

Planet Legless

Read the problem.

On Planet Legless there are aliens that have no legs just arms.

There are several 'species':

Bimen with two arms

Trimen with three arms

Quadmen with four arms

Quinmen with five arms.

One day the Bimen and Trimen were having a picnic.

They were all waving their arms about.

29 arms could be seen.

How many Bimen and Trimen were there?

Aliens ahoy!

Name _____ **Date** _____

Which times table help may help you? Talk about why.

Write your thinking here.

Is it helpful to make lists of the multiples?

What do we know about adding odd and even numbers together?

What do we always get when we add two even numbers?

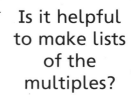

Now make up a problem.

What do we always get when we add two odd numbers?

How can this information help you?

What do we always get when we add one of each?

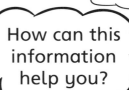

What total of arms are you looking for?

Are there any numbers you know you can't use? Is it helpful to cross them out?

Have you found all the possible answers? How do you know?

What do you need to know?

BRIEF

In 'What do you need to know?' the children are asked to work out how much some items from a selection of shops cost. The activity involves sorting clues, some relevant, some not and logically working out how they can be used to find a solution to the problem. There is also an element of simple algebra in this activity. It gives you the opportunity to hear the children's reasoning and thinking as they work out their solutions.

Key maths links

- Making decisions
- Reasoning about numbers
- Calculations
- Money

Thinking skills

- Information processing
- Locate and classify relevant information
- Analyze relationships

Language

total amount, spend, price, cost, change, mass, because, so
What could I try next? I think this …

Resources

PCM 3 (one per pair and enlarged copy of fishmonger's statements cut out)
PCM 4 (one per pair)
paper
pens or pencils
scissors

1 Setting the scene

Make up a short story about Sam, who is going shopping for his family. In your story he must visit a fishmonger, baker, chemist and grocer. Tell the children that their task is to find out how much he spent on each item that he bought.
If they have not tackled an activity like this before, work through the first problem from PCM 3 together. Read the statements to the children. *Can these help us find out the cost of the fish? Which ones will? Why won't these? What do you **need** to know?* Once you have established that some are helpful, display them and discard those that are not. *What is the first thing we must know before we can do anything else? Why? Which clues are more helpful at this stage? How can we sort these statements?* Group the statements like this:

Sam gave Mark £5   Sam bought 2 salmon
He received 20p change   Sam bought 6 sardines

1 salmon costs the same as 3 sardines

Ask the children to talk to a friend and try to work out the solution. When someone has found one, ask them to explain how they got it. Reinforce the idea of substitution, i.e. changing the salmon for sardines or vice versa.

2 Getting started

Ask the children to work in pairs or small groups to solve the other three problems. Give them each a statement sheet, making sure all the shops are represented. The main group of children should begin by working on the grocer's shop. Remind them that their first task is to cut out the statements and sort them into a useful pile and a not useful pile. After the children have found the solutions, ask them to take Sam to a DIY shop and make up a similar set of statements so that the class can try to solve how much three items cost.

Simplify

Use the statements about the baker's shop. If these prove to be too difficult, write your own prices in the appropriate places. If they prove to be easily solved try those on PCM 4.

Challenge

Use the statements for the chemist's shop.

Checkpoints

Encourage the children to talk about and listen to each other's thinking; particularly initially when they decide which clues are relevant. If any pairs are having difficulty knowing which clues to make use of first, discuss each clue with them and whether it is useful at this point. Bring the class, or groups tackling the same problem, together to check the progress they are making.

Watch out for ...

Watch out for children that show the ability to rationalize the clues, apply logical thinking and the ability to substitute in order to find a common denominator. Invite these to share their ideas.
It is also important to look out for good discussion.

Ask ...

- *Why are those clues important?*
- *How are you going to get started?*
- *What do we know about the cost of ... and the cost of ...?*
- *How will what you know help you to find a solution?*

Listen for ...

Listen for discussion about why certain clues are necessary. Observe the children working through their thinking about why certain foods can be substituted for others and what that will mean.

Moving on ...

Review the solutions the children found. Did they make sense within the context of the problem? Make a list of all the items and their costs. Ask the children to find the total Sam spent. Ask them if it was helpful to work with a partner. *Why? What can make group or pair work difficult?*
Invite the children working on the DIY problem to share their work with the class and encourage the class to work together to find a solution using the thinking they used for their own activities.

Where next?

- Try the same type of activity, where appropriate, during a science, history or geography lesson.
- The activity can be altered to suit other year groups by using appropriate amounts of money and increased/decreased complexity of substitutions.
- Use this idea in word problem solving activities.

What did you learn from the puzzles that the children set? Did they understand what to do? Did any of them come up with good 'red herrings'? The subtlety of these are often the best indicator of their understanding. Did any of the children achieve more than you had anticipated?

DEBRIEF

Sam's problems

Name _____ **Date** _____

Sam went shopping. What did he buy in each shop? How much did he spend on each item? Cut out the statements and take the ones that will help you.

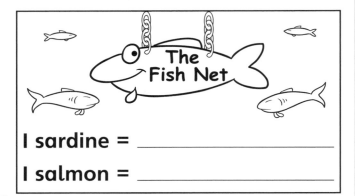

I sardine = _____

I salmon = _____

I roll   = _____

I baguette = _____

The shop is called **The Fish Net**	The shop is called **The Crusty Loaf**
Sam bought 6 sardines	Sam bought 4 rolls
He went into the fishmonger's at 11:00	The rolls weigh 200 g each
Sam bought 2 salmon	He went into the baker's at 10:15 a.m.
The shopkeeper is called Mark	The shopkeeper is called Pedro
Sam gave Mark £5	Sam gave Pedro £3
He received 80p change	Sam bought 2 baguettes
I salmon costs the same as 3 sardines	He received 60p change
He spent 15 minutes there	4 rolls cost the same as 1 baguette
6 sardines are the same weight as 2 salmon	The baguette weighs twice as much as 4 rolls

More problems for Sam

Name _____ Date _____

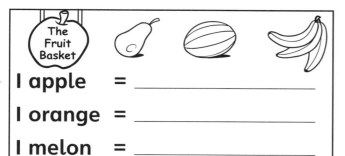

1 apple	= _____
1 orange	= _____
1 melon	= _____

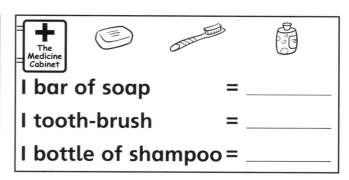

1 bar of soap	= _____
1 tooth-brush	= _____
1 bottle of shampoo	= _____

The shop is called **The Fruit Basket**	The shop is called **The Medicine Cabinet**
Sam bought 3 apples	Sam bought 2 bars of soap
6 apples weigh the same as 1 melon	1 bar of soap weighs 250 g
He went into the grocer's at half past 11	He went into the chemist's at 11:45 a.m.
Sam bought 2 oranges	Sam bought 3 tooth-brushes
The shopkeeper is called Chrissie	The shopkeeper is called Cindy
Sam gave Chrissie £4	Sam gave Cindy £20
Sam bought 1 melon	Sam bought 4 bottles of shampoo
He received 40p change	He received £5 change
1 melon costs the same as 3 apples and 2 oranges	2 bottles of shampoo cost the same as 4 tooth-brushes
3 oranges and 2 apples weigh the same as a pineapple	3 bars of soap weigh the same as a bottle of shampoo
6 apples cost the same as 2 oranges	2 bars of soap cost the same as 1 tooth-brush

Assessing progress

You know that children are developing their skills in information processing when they start to make connections with different mathematical ideas. They should start to show and use this understanding in other lessons. This might be by applying mathematical knowledge in a new situation or it might be in the way that they go about a subsequent task. As their skills in using information develop they should become more precise in the way that they use mathematical language and more systematic in their approach to working and to recording. The techniques that they have used should be developed in other subjects so that their understanding of information processing skills can be transferred to other areas of the curriculum.

Cross-curricular thinking

Little Red Riding Hood, Snow White and Cinderella – who is the odd one out? Why? What makes the other two the same?

Literacy

A strategy like 'odd one out' can be used to compare characters from fictional genres, such as different heroines from traditional tales.

Art

The 'odd one out' strategy is also useful for comparing the work of famous artists or to look at similarities and differences in the visual and tactile qualities of materials.

Science

Venn diagrams are powerful tools in the teaching of classification. This is particularly valuable in the strands of both variation and classification of living things, and materials and their properties.

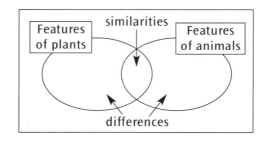

History

Venn diagrams are useful to teach how to compare and contrast in history. Two intersecting sets can be used as a planning tool to identify similarities and differences between different historical periods. Common features go in the intersection and contrasting information on each side.

Geography

The 'odd one out' strategy and Venn diagrams are both helpful in geography. The former can be used to encourage children to use geographical vocabulary as they talk about what makes three different landscapes or features of the environment similar or different. The latter can be used for sorting pictures of buildings or vocabulary related to the character of places. This way, the children will develop an understanding of these concepts by having examples and counter-examples to talk about in a meaningful context.

That's because ...
Reasoning skills

> **Reasoning** – these skills enable pupils to give reasons for opinions and actions, to draw inferences and make deductions, to use precise language to explain what they think and to make judgements and decisions informed by reasons or evidence. (QCA 2000)

Overview

This unit is about reasoning and logical thinking. Reasoning is an essential aspect of mathematics and underpins the development of theorems and proofs through the use of precise definitions and axioms. For pupils of primary age it is important that they have the opportunity to apply their knowledge and understanding of mathematical ideas and concepts logically and systematically as this will enable them to make connections between different concepts and between different areas of mathematics. This will deepen their understanding and develop their confidence as well as helping them see how mathematics can be used as a practical tool in their daily lives.

Developing reasoning skills is also about developing habits of thinking or dispositions as much as it is about specific logical skills. Of course, just because you are good at reasoning does not mean that you are going to be reasonable. Part of thinking reasonably is also dependent upon your knowledge of yourself and the situation in which you find yourself. This metacognitive dimension is essential if you are going to help your pupils become effective thinkers and not just logical.

Strategies

Reasoning skills can be broken down further into the following kinds of behaviours or activities that pupils can do:
- **Give reasons for opinions and actions**
  explain, say because, say why
- **Draw inferences and make deductions**
  see links, make connections, infer, deduce, use words like 'so', 'then', 'must be', 'has to be'
- **Use precise language to explain what they think**
  exemplify, describe, define, characterize
- **Make judgements and decisions informed by reasons or evidence**
  form an opinion, determine, conclude, summarize, *especially where there is more than one course of action or possible solution*

Questions

Explain why ...? Can you give a reason ...? Because ... So ...
Why is ... an example? Is that always/sometimes/never true? What else must be true if ... ? Does it have to be like that? Can you define that? What do they all have in common?
What else is like that? What makes you say that? How can you be sure that ...?

I can, I can't

BRIEF

The children are provided with a series of statements and eight shapes. They need to see if they can make each statement an 'I can' statement. One of the purposes of the task is to link creativity with reasoning in order to gain a flexibility to think 'outside' the confines of stereotypical regular shapes and think more about irregular ones. It will also give you the opportunity to listen to their reasoning behind making 'I can' or 'I can't' statements. This activity will also give you the opportunity to check out their understanding of the properties of the polygons they have learned about.

Key maths links

- Properties of 2D shape

Thinking skills

- Reasoning
- Draw inferences
- Make deductions
- Use of precise language
- Creativity

Language

polygon, square, oblong, rectangle, pentagon, hexagon, heptagon, octagon, isosceles triangle, equilateral triangle, regular, irregular, properties, lines of symmetry, must be, so, then, because

Resources

regular 3- to 8-sided polygons
PCM 5 (one each)
PCM 6 (one each and enlarged copy of shapes)
scissors
pens or pencils
paper
rulers

 Setting the scene

Show the children the regular three- to eight-sided polygons and rehearse their names and properties, including that of symmetry. Ask the children what they notice about the number of lines of symmetry in each shape. Draw some irregular shapes on the board and repeat questioning about their properties. Show one of the statements and, using the large set of squares and isosceles triangles (that are half the squares), invite a pupil to try to make the shape on the statement. Invite another pupil to try to make the shape in a different way.

 Getting started

Ask the children to work in pairs. They need to cut out the shapes on PCM 5 and use all of them each time to make the shape specified in the 'I can' statements like a jig-saw puzzle with different pictures. They need to sketch the shapes they make on paper showing where the pieces go. Once they have done this they then need to use PCM 6 to try and find as many different ways of making them as possible.

Simplify

The children working at an easier level can use just as many shapes as they need to make the shape for an 'I can' statement, which won't necessarily be all of them.

Challenge

Once the children have completed this task, ask: *What if you use four oblongs and four equilateral triangles? Can you still make these 'I can' statements?* Give them some paper and a pair of scissors and ask them to try. Ask them to try to make the same shapes as they did before.

 Checkpoints

Once the children have started to work, sit amongst a group for a while and listen to their talk as they work. It is important that they share their ideas and listen to each other. Ask them how are they thinking as they put the small shapes together to make the one on the statement. Introduce a mini-plenary every so often so that you can promote good listening and discussion by using pairs of children that you have observed working well together as examples, inviting them to share some of their solutions with the rest of the class. Highlight examples of reasoning, such as when children say, *It must go there* or *If we turn that round it will make it a hexagon.*

Watch out for ...

Look for children who are working well together by listening to each other, those who are using the shapes in different orientations and those who are using their previous shape as a starting point for the next one. Make sure they realize that a hexagon is just a six-sided figure (it does not have to be a regular hexagon).

Ask ...

- *What shape will you make if you put that there?*
- *Is there another position where you can place that and make the same type of shape?*
- *How did you make that shape?*
- *How can you use this shape for the next statement?*
- *What were you thinking as you did that?*

Listen for ...

Encourage children who are making sensible deductions, *This has already got 5 sides, if we put that there that will be 2 more and we only need 7* and *If we turn this upside down it will fit in there and not give us any extra sides.* Also listen for comments that use appropriate vocabulary for reasoning, for example, *If I put this here that must be an irregular pentagon because it has 5 sides and angles which are different.*

Moving on ...

Review some of the shapes that the children have been able to make. Ask: *Has anyone been able to make a regular shape?* Invite a few children to have a go. Ask: *Do you think it is possible to make one? Why/why not?*

Where next?

- Use pairs of different shapes.
- Try this practically with cubes and pyramids – what shapes can they make with sets of these?

Were the children able to express themselves clearly? What questioning did you use to encourage this? Were they flexible in their manipulation of the shapes? Did they show creativity? Did many complete the challenge? What were their findings? Is there any way in which you could improve this activity or extend it further?

DEBRIEF

I can, I can't

Name _____ **Date** _____

Cut out the shapes below. You need 4 squares and 4 triangles.

Put them together to try to make each of these shapes. Draw your shapes.

I can ☐ can't ☐ make a pentagon.

I can ☐ can't ☐ make a hexagon.

I can ☐ can't ☐ make an isosceles triangle.

I can ☐ can't ☐ make an equilateral triangle.

I can ☐ can't ☐ make a heptagon.

I can ☐ can't ☐ make an octagon.

I can ☐ can't ☐ make a quadrilateral.

I can ☐ can't ☐ make a parallelogram.

Squares and triangles

Name _____ Date _____

Now use the squares and triangles from PCM 5 to make as many shapes as you can.

They must all be different!

Draw the shapes you made and make a list of their properties.

Remember the properties of 2D shapes include number of sides, number of corners and the number of lines of symmetry.

Up the mountain

BRIEF

In 'Up the mountain' the children work their way up the mountain path by finding links between adjoining numbers. They then make up their own 'path' identifying as many links as they can. They need to think of possible criteria and exclude those that don't fit, giving reasons for those that do. This involves sorting, comparing and contrasting the properties of the numbers involved.

Key maths links

- Properties of number
- Place value
- Reasoning about numbers

Thinking skills

- Give reasons for opinions
- Draw inferences
- Use precise language
- Make judgements

Language

square numbers, multiples, thousands, hundreds, halves, doubles, digits, fractions, explain, because, so

Resources

PCM 7 (one per pair)
PCM 8 (one each)
two sets of 0–9 digit cards
calculators

 ## Setting the scene

Invite four children to pick a digit card each from your two sets. Pair them to make 2-digit numbers, e.g. 3 6 9 4, put together to give 64 and 39. Explain to the children that they are looking for properties that are the same in both numbers. Ask them to tell you some that they notice, such as both are even, both 2-digit numbers, both are multiples of 4, both are square numbers. Repeat this with eight cards, making two 4-digit numbers, e.g. 1589 and 1683: both are 4-digit numbers, both are odd, both have 1 in the thousands position and 8 in the tens, both have an odd units number. Let the children use calculators to check their thinking.

 ## Getting started

Give the children PCM 7 showing the mountain and the number trail. They work in pairs and put a counter at 50. Then they identify similarities and links between 50 and the next number, which is 100. They should discuss their ideas and justify their thinking to each other. Encourage them to look at such things as place value, multiples and factors. When they have found as many similarities as they can, they record them either on the PCM or on paper and move their counter to the next number (100), where they must again find similarities between the 100 and 225. This continues until they reach the top of the mountain. When they have completed this task, encourage the children to make their own 'trail' on PCM 8.

Simplify

The children can work with you, a Teaching Assistant, or in a mixed ability pair to look for one or two similarities concentrating on place value and multiples. When they reach the top they make their own 'trail' using numbers that have at least one similarity.

Challenge

The children can look for at least four similarities and links (some have as many as seven or eight properties in common). When they reach the top, they make their own 'trail' using numbers that have at least three similarities.

Checkpoints

Gather the class for a mini-plenary to discuss what they have found so far and to remind them of properties to look for, with 'opt out' points when the children can choose whether to stay for more discussion or return to continue their work. Ask them to identify good numbers for similarities and hence 'easy moves' and more challenging pairs of numbers for 'difficult moves'. This will give you good feedback about their understanding of number properties. Challenge them to make a mountain trail which has at least five similarities for each step.

Watch out for ...

It is important that the children explore each number. Are they looking for similarities in place value, multiples etc? Are they making deductions? E.g. if that is a multiple of 8, then it must be a multiple of 4 and 2. Can they find similarities that haven't been suggested? E.g. prime numbers, fractions of each other.

Ask ...

- ❍ *What is the same about these two numbers?*
- ❍ *What else are they a multiple of?*
- ❍ *What makes you think they are both square numbers?*
- ❍ *What else must be true if they are both even numbers/multiples of 10/multiples of 9 ...?*

Listen for ...

Are the children discussing the relationships between each pair of numbers? How articulate are they at describing these relationships?

Moving on ...

Find out who got to the top of the mountain. Ask a few of the children to choose pairs of numbers and explain the similarities that they found. Can the rest of the children find any more? Which two numbers had the most similarities? Invite one or two to share their own mountain trail and ask the class to try to get to the top.

Where next?

- ❍ Use this idea for similarities in the various properties of shapes.
- ❍ Make a materials or living things chain in science where each item has to have one, two or three properties or characteristics in common with the item next to it.
- ❍ Identify similarities in the work of different artists in terms of styles and techniques.

Did the mini-plenary and opt out idea work? Did any of the children surprise you with more complex similarities? Think about the way you introduced the activity. Was there enough input or would more examples have helped? Were you happy with the way the children recorded their work or could this have been improved?

DEBRIEF

Names _____ **Date** _____

Find the links between the numbers.

Are they multiples of the same number?

Are any of the digits the same?

Are they odd or even?

Do they have any of the same factors?

How many digits are there?

What are they divisible by?

TOP

7920

792

297

99

3223

4114

144

64

320

960

1920

1233

225

100

50

START

Name _____ **Date** _____

Make your own trail
up the mountain.

TOP

Are they multiples
of the same number?

Do they have any of
the same factors?

Are any of the
digits the same?

How many
digits are there?

Are they odd
or even?

What are they
divisible by?

START

Assessing progress

You know that children are developing their reasoning skills when they start using words like 'because', 'then' and 'so' in their discussions and their responses to your questions. They may also start to ask each other 'why?' questions and seek explanations from each other (and from you). Giving reasons as part of explanations then becomes a routine part of thinking lessons. Once you start to ask children why (or to ask another child why a response either was or was not correct) you will be able to assess the reasons in their responses. You need to ensure you ask children to justify correct and incorrect responses, otherwise they will 'read' your question as meaning they have made a mistake if you only ask 'why?' when an answer is wrong. Once children get used to this you can simply wait encouragingly or say 'because...?' to get them to extend their replies to your questions to assess their reasoning skills.

Cross-curricular thinking

Science

Asking a question such as, *What will happen if?* is a good starting point for scientific reasoning. *What will happen if you put a tea cosy over an icy drink? Will it warm up faster or more slowly? What will happen if you drop a football and a cannonball from the top of a tall building? Will the cannonball reach the ground first?* Using thought provoking questions like these can stimulate scientific reasoning (as well as revealing children's thinking about scientific concepts).

History

A strategy like 'odd one out' can also be used to develop reasoning skills as the children are asked to give reasons for their choice of an 'odd one out' and can be encouraged to distinguish between historical and non-historical reasons. Choose three famous people and ask children to identify an odd one out with a historical reason.

Literacy

Justifying choices of words and phrases is a good way both to develop reasoning, and model thinking about composition. Asking a series of questions such as, *Why did you choose that adjective or powerful verb? What others did you consider? Why did you reject those?*, not only gives children the opportunity to give their reasons, but to make them explicit for others to hear.

Geography

Geographical enquiry is supported by reasoning as children express their views about places or changes to the environment. They can use a technique, such as identifying 'Plus, minus and interesting' points to compile a table, then justify the points they have identified with reasons.

Detective work
Enquiry skills

> **Enquiry** – these skills enable pupils to ask relevant questions, to pose and define problems, to plan what to do and how to carry out research, to predict outcomes and anticipate responses, to test conclusions and improve ideas. (QCA 2000)

Overview

Enquiry skills are as much a way of working or developing particular habits of mind which keep a range of possibilities open for as long as possible. The process of enquiry is about being flexible, looking for alternatives and testing a range of possible solutions. In mathematics these are essential skills as enquiry develops an understanding of relationships and connections that may not be immediately obvious.

The process of enquiry is at the heart of learning. It is only when you can identify what you need to know, go through a process of finding out and be able to recognize when you have found a solution that you can undertake independent learning. Enquiry skills can, therefore, best be developed in situations where it is not possible to see a solution from the outset and where children will benefit from working together.

There are good opportunities for speaking and listening in presenting the results of an investigation or enquiry. Enquiry lessons are also excellent for review and reflection about the process of learning.

The challenge for the teacher is at the beginning and end of the enquiry process. It is difficult to instruct children in how to ask relevant questions without directing them to a particular investigation or mathematical problem. Similarly, it is difficult enough for pupils to recognize that they have come up with a solution to an investigation, without them realizing that it is a good solution. Identifying what would be a better answer is even more difficult - challenging even for adults! Enquiry skills are also therefore, about developing more systematic habits of questioning as well as the specific skills in solving a problem.

Strategies

Enquiry skills can be broken down further into the following kinds of behaviours or activities that pupils can do:
- ◗ **Ask relevant questions**
  Enquire, be curious, ask, probe, investigate
- ◗ **Pose and define problems**
  Frame, propose, suggest, put forward an idea
- ◗ **Plan what to do and how to research**
  Think out, plan, sketch, formulate or organize ideas
- ◗ **Predict outcomes and anticipate responses**
  Suppose, predict, guess, estimate, approximate, foresee
- ◗ **Test conclusions and improve ideas**
  Experiment, test, improve, refine, revise, amend, perfect

Questions

Show me how you could ...? What might work? What ideas have you got? What is a good question to ask? How could you find out? How could you check? Any predictions? What is your best guess? What are you expecting? About how much will it be?

Who dunnit?

BRIEF

In 'Who dunnit?' the children are asked to find the perpetrator of a crime using the concept of proportion. The activity involves looking at evidence left at a 'crime scene' and using that, along with information that they must work out for themselves, to find the person/s responsible. Enquiry skills are used within the topics of proportion and/or length.

Key maths links

- Using ideas of simple proportion
- Length

Thinking skills

- Enquiry
- Ask relevant questions
- Pose and define problems
- Predict outcomes

Language

proportion, one for every ..., centimetres, circumference, metres, predictions, why?, what could ...?

Resources

PCM 9 (one per pair)
PCM 10 (one per pair)
tape measures
paper strips (4 cm wide and 45 cm long)
paper
pens and pencils

Setting the scene

Make up a short story about a robbery, murder or other crime and tell it to the class. It needs to include these facts:
- two things were left at the scene – a hat and a glove
- the length of the glove was 27 cm from tip of middle finger to wrist
- the circumference of the hat was 56 cm
- there were eight suspects, who are pictured on PCM 9 and PCM 10, with their names and their heights.

Explain to the children that they are going to be detectives and try to work out who committed the crime. Say that their only equipment will be themselves, a tape measure, a pair of scissors and strips of paper, plus pen and paper to record their findings.

Getting started

Ask: *Do you think this hat and this glove can help us find out who committed the crime? Do you think putting the heights of the people on their pictures is relevant?* Once you have established that all three are probably important, ask the children to work with a partner to try to think why. After a short while ask the children for their thoughts. Aim towards the idea that the distance around their heads and the length of their hands (from tip of middle finger to wrist) are connected to their heights.

Ask the children to work in pairs or small groups to find out how these lengths are connected and what they can do using the tape measure, strips of paper, scissors and themselves to work out a way to solve this problem.

Simplify

Use either the glove or the hat to find one guilty person. Encourage the children to make a strip of paper the same length as their height and one to match their hand measurement, and then see how many times the hand fits into the length. It will be roughly nine times. Discuss how this will help.

Challenge

Ask the children to work out what the lengths of gloves and the circumferences of hats would be if the other people were guilty. Encourage them to make up similar stories with some of the others in the pictures involved.

Checkpoints

Stop the class after a short period of time to discuss the initial approaches they have made. If necessary guide the children towards finding connections by asking them to compare the length of their hand (from tip of middle finger to wrist) with their height. Then ask how that might help in this problem. If necessary, repeat for the circumference of their heads and their heights. Ask them to compare findings.

Watch out for ...

Check that the children measure accurately. Circumferences are particularly tricky. Also check out their ability to recognize the connections between the body parts, i.e. three head circumferences are equivalent to one height and nine hand lengths to one height. Are they able to make these connections in order to solve the problem? Some children will benefit from working practically with the strips of paper, so ensure that they have the opportunity to see the relationship (sticking alternating different colours of paper to make a hand length 'ruler' may help).

Ask ...

- ❍ *Have you any predictions? What makes you think that?*
- ❍ *What ideas have you got to get started?*
- ❍ *What is the relationship between the hand and height measurements?*
- ❍ *How could you use this relationship to find out who did it?*

Listen for ...

Listen for discussion about how their measurements relate to each other and how this information can be used to solve the problem.

 Moving on ...

Who solved the problem? Ask one or two of the children to describe to the class how they approached the work and what conclusions they reached. Do the rest of the children agree? Would this evidence stand up in court? What evidence would you need to be convinced of 'who dunnit'?

Where next?

- ❍ Is there a proportional relationship between foot size and height?
- ❍ Is the relationship more obvious in adults than children?
- ❍ What counts as evidence? For a policeman? In history?

How often did you intervene? Were your interventions necessary? Would the children benefit from repeating this activity but identifying a different culprit? Did you think it was important to let the children work practically with the strips of paper, or wasn't it necessary for some?

DEBRIEF

The suspects

Find out 'who dunnit'.

Harvey

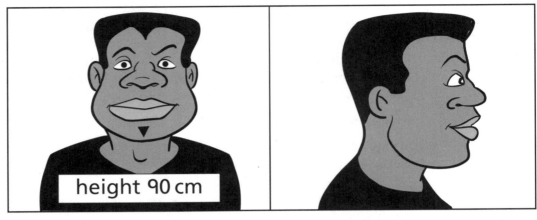

height 90 cm

Claudette

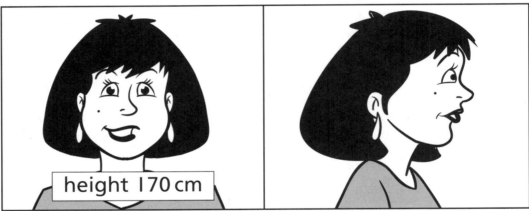

height 170 cm

Bertha

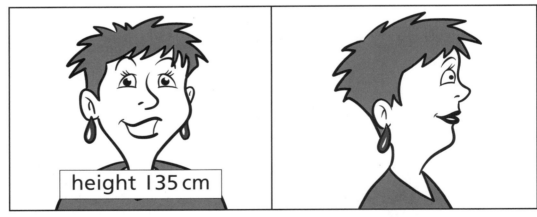

height 135 cm

Sid

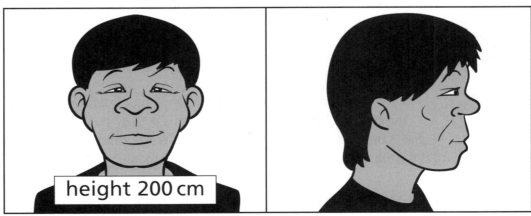

height 200 cm

Find out 'who dunnit'.

Rummpel

height 240 cm

Rolf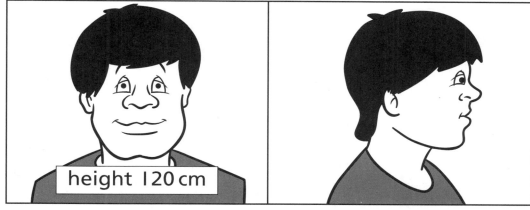

height 120 cm

Frank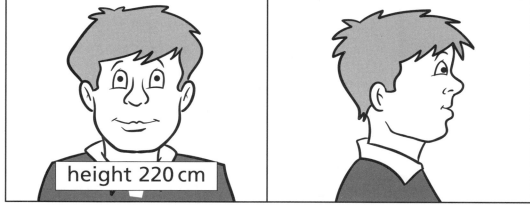

height 220 cm

Jimmy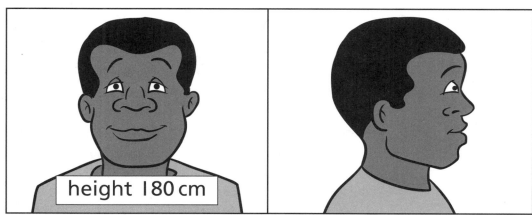

height 180 cm

Mystery numbers

In 'Mystery numbers' the children are asked to find the possible missing numbers to complete a number grid and formulate a rule for generating all the possibilities. Each grid concentrates on one of each of the four rules of addition, subtraction, multiplication and division. This is an 'open' problem with a variety of answers and ways of reaching them. The children have to plan how to carry out the task, make predictions and come to conclusions which need testing.

Key maths links

- Reasoning about numbers
- Making decisions
- Calculations: +, −, ×, ÷

Thinking skills

- Enquiry
- Ask relevant questions
- Predict outcomes
- Test conclusions

Language

add, total, subtract, difference, multiply, divide, predict, test

Resources

PCM 11 (one per pair)
PCM 12 (one per pair)
calculators (optional)

Setting the scene

Show some number grids that have numbers missing, one for each rule, e.g.:

	12	15
18	30	?
24	?	?

	40	56
32	?	?
60	20	?

	6	10
13	78	?
21	?	?

	18	90
6	?	?
3	6	?

Ask the children to work out which operation each grid requires (+, −, ×, ÷) and, as a class, fill in the missing numbers. Ask the children how they found the operation and the numbers. Discuss how straightforward this exercise was and why. Highlight the fact that it was a closed problem with only one answer and only one way of finding it. Tell the children that they will be working on similar problems, but instead of finding the answers for the middle of the grid they will have to work out the numbers that go around the outside.

Getting started

Show one of the number grids from PCM 11 that the children will be using and ask: *Do you think there will just be one answer for this?* Give the children a few minutes to talk about this with a neighbour, and then ask them to share and explain their thinking with the rest of the class. Invite them to offer suggestions as to what one of the numbers may be. Discuss whether this is the only one it could be, invite other ideas. After they have completed the grids and come up with a rule or reason to show how other numbers that will fit in the grid can be generated, expect the children to make up challenging number grid puzzles and evaluate what makes a good one.

The children need to work in pairs or small groups.

Simplify

Use PCM 11 and ask the children to answer the addition grid first, thinking of a rule to make other numbers to fit it. Once they have finished, if time, move on to the subtraction grid.

Challenge

Use PCM 12. Expect their explanations to include the fact that once numbers have been found, they can be manipulated to make others, i.e. addition: increase the outside numbers of columns by one or two, decrease those of the rows by the same amount and vice versa; subtraction: increase or decrease both; multiplication:

double rows or columns and halve the other; division: double or halve both, multiply by 10 or 100. Get them to evaluate which were difficult and why.

3 Checkpoints

Stop the class after a short period of time to discuss the initial approaches they have made. Ask the pairs to work in fours to share what they have done so far. Invite a few children to tell the whole class some of the numbers they found that worked in their grids.

Watch out for ...

Look out for children making inaccurate calculations and check a few, as making mistakes will have an impact on the whole grid. Ensure the children are thinking systematically, using what they knew to generate more numbers, rather than pure trial and error. Work with them using trial and error to point them in the right direction.

Ask ...

- ● *What do you have to do?*
- ● *How might you get started?*
- ● *What can you do to both those numbers to get this answer again?*
- ● *If you add one to that number, what must you do to this one? Can you tell me why?*
- ● *Can you show me what it is you are doing?*

Listen for ...

Listen for discussion about altering numbers by adding or subtracting one or two in order to make other numbers that will work. If you hear this type of talk going on, stop the class and ask those you heard to explain their thinking.

4 Moving on ...

Ask the children to get into their groups of four, as before, and talk to each other about their results. Then, invite a few groups to tell the whole class what conclusions they reached.

Where next?

- ● Investigate grids like this with shapes and colours.
- ● Ask the children to design their own puzzles.

Was it valuable for two pairs to get together to share before feeding back to the rest of the class? Would you do this again? Were the numbers in the grids pitched at the right level or would they have been better modified? Were the children able to make up challenging number grid puzzles? What was their thinking on what made a good one?

DEBRIEF

3 by 3 number grids

Name _____ **Date** _____

Complete the number grids. Find different ways for each grid.
Show your workings.

1

+		
	18	
	22	24

+		
	18	
	22	24

+		
	18	
	22	24

workings

2

−		
	11	3
		6

−		
	11	3
		6

−		
	11	3
		6

3

×		
	32	
	80	120

×		
	32	
	80	120

×		
	32	
	80	120

4

÷		
	3	4
		8

÷		
	3	4
		8

÷		
	3	4
		8

Make up your own number grid.

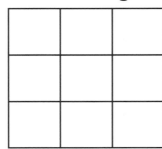

Name _____ **Date** _____

Complete the number grids. Find different ways for each grid.
Show your workings.

1

+			
	115		108
119	135		
		159	136

+			
	115		108
119	135		
		159	136

+			
	115		108
119	135		
		159	136

workings

2

−			
		167	62
4			22
70	193		

−			
		167	62
4			22
70	193		

−			
		167	62
4			22
70	193		

3

×			
48	72		
	138	115	
144		180	

×			
48	72		
	138	115	
144		180	

×			
48	72		
	138	115	
144		180	

4

÷			
	24		
60	36	30	
	42		

÷			
	24		
60	36	30	
	42		

÷			
	24		
60	36	30	
	42		

Make up your own number grid.

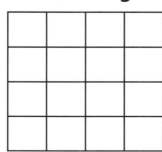

Assessing progress

Evidence that children are making progress in developing enquiry skills can be gained by observing the way that they are working. Enquiry is as much a habit, or an attitude, keeping a range of possibilities open for as long as possible. Being flexible, looking for alternatives and testing a range of possible solutions are therefore good indications that enquiry skills are developing.

Cross-curricular thinking

Literacy

Another variation on the 'Living graphs' (page 22) strategy is developing the understanding of narratives, both in fiction and non-fiction texts (such as historical narratives), through discussion and enquiry. The graph is replaced with a 'fortune line' about a character's feelings or mood. The children place statements from the narrative on the graph. To do this they need to sequence the text and empathize with the character. Investigating a number of similar narratives (such as traditional tales) will show that they tend to have a similar shaped graph, reflecting the narrative structure and the use of repetition to develop suspense (in *The Three Billy Goats Gruff* and *Little Red Riding Hood*, for example).

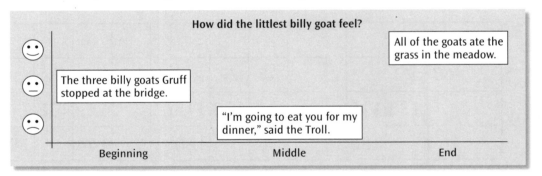

History

Fortune lines can also be used in historical enquiry particularly to develop empathy, the statements can either come from real historical figures (the diaries of Samuel Pepys and Anne Frank are good sources) or characters created for the task (such as a child miner in Victorian times).

Science

Developing scientific enquiry means the children must think up questions that can be investigated. An approach called 'Philosophy for children' has been shown to encourage children to develop questioning skills. It uses a stimulus as a starting point, commonly a familiar story, but it can be a poem or a picture, that the children think up questions about. They then select one to answer in a class discussion called a 'community of enquiry'. It is possible to extend this into science where questions can be investigated and you can challenge the children to work out how they could find out the answer.

Geography

This approach can work in geography, particularly when a photograph of an interesting landscape is used as the starting point. After a discussion of what the children think, their motivation to find out is likely to be enhanced.

What if ...?

Creative thinking skills

> **Creative thinking** – these skills enable pupils to generate and extend ideas, to suggest hypotheses, to apply imagination and to look for alternative, innovative outcomes. (QCA 2000)

Overview

Creative thinking is the kind of thinking that produces new insights, approaches, or perspectives. It is essential in education that learners see that they can come up with new ideas or suggestions which help their own thinking as well as stimulating the thinking of others. No one expects a 7- or 11-year-old to come up with something unique in the history of human development, but unless we value the creativity that young children naturally have they will stop thinking creatively and rely on reproducing ideas they have been given by others.

Creativity is often *not* associated with mathematics in schools, but thinking up new solutions to problems, seeing new connections, or thinking of more efficient or effective alternatives is what mathematicians do. It is not necessary for the ideas to be completely original, just new for the individual pupil or shared with the class for the first time, or it might be that ideas or concepts are seen in a new or unusual way. It is important that pupils feel comfortable in order to be creative. They need to have confidence that their ideas will be accepted and that there is a range of possible answers or solutions to a problem or issue. The aim is to encourage pupils to think up a range of ideas, to have new thoughts or ideas (at least for them) or to extend and develop other people's ideas.

There are a number of techniques and approaches to support creative thinking such as brainstorming, thinking of analogies, visualizing or picturing possibilities. What all these techniques have in common is an emphasis on the flow of ideas. This means that in the early stages of supporting creative thinking it is essential to be uncritical to ensure that thinking is not too restricted.

Strategies

Creative thinking skills can be broken down further into the following kinds of behaviours or activities that pupils can do:
- **Generate and extend ideas**
  Brainstorm, think up, develop, extend
- **Suggest hypotheses**
  Suppose, surmise (*use phrases like 'how about ...?', 'it could be ...'*)
- **Apply imagination**
  Design, devise, visualize, elaborate
- **Look for alternative, innovative outcomes**
  Think laterally, fancy, guestimate, invent

Questions

Can you imagine? What would that look like? How could you change it to make it a ... ? Can you think of a question you could ask? Go on ... What will the answer look like? Another idea? And another ...

Tell me a story

BRIEF

In 'Tell me a story' the children are asked to generate digital clock times using digit cards, draw them on an analogue clock, order the times and then create stories using these times. They need to consider all possible times that can be made using the three digit cards that they pick and give reasons why they can't make any times, e.g. 4:65 doesn't exist.

Key maths links

- Read the time from an analogue clock and 12 hour digital to the nearest minute
- Use a.m. and p.m. and the notation 4:57
- Reasoning about numbers
- Making decisions
- Place value

Thinking skills

- Generate and extend ideas
- Suggest hypotheses
- Apply imagination

Language

minutes, hours, analogue, digital, a.m., p.m., visualize, suppose

Resources

PCM 13 (one per pair)
PCM 14 (one per pair)
analogue clock (with movable hands) (one per child)
pens and pencils
scissors

1 Setting the scene

Ask the children to find some analogue and digital times on their clocks, e.g. 20 minutes to 11, 5:27. Make up some problems, for example: *My watch says 25 minutes past 6, it is 10 minutes slow, show me what time it is really. The bus leaves in 17 minutes, it is now 11:46. Show me what time it will leave.*

Write three numbers on the board and draw the colon that separates the minute numbers from the hours. Invite someone to use the numbers to make a time. Write a.m. beside the time and discuss what the difference would be if you had written p.m. Ask if there is another time that could be made using the same numbers. Find out the difference between the two times. Ask for suggestions about a story that could go with the times. Encourage creative suggestions.

2 Getting started

The children should work in pairs. Each pair will need a set of digit cards face down in front of them and a colon. They pick three cards, make the earliest a.m. or p.m. time or mixture of both around the colon, draw and label it on PCM 13. They then rearrange the cards and make the next time in sequence. Repeat this until all possible times are found. Encourage the use of a time line, if appropriate. Once they have found all possibilities, they find the differences between them, and make up a creative short story to include both times and time differences, e.g.

Times from earliest to latest: 3:56 p.m., 5:36 p.m., 6:35 p.m., 6:53 p.m.

Story: I got home from school at 3:56 p.m., my mum didn't expect me until 5:36, so I was 1 hour and 40 minutes early. At 6:35 I fed and played with my hamster for 18 minutes until 6:53, then I went out to play with a friend.

Simplify

Ask the children to make two times using the digit cards, say which is going to be their earliest and then draw that one and then the second. Make up a short story, using the time and its difference. Let the children use clocks to help them if necessary. Offer some suggestions as to where the story might take place such as 'At the zoo' or 'The dentist'.

Challenge

After they have finished the original task, ask the children to pick three cards and use them to make a length of time, e.g. 4 , 5 , 9 time length: 9 hours 45 minutes. Next they should find two clock times with that difference. Can they find another? Ask them to try to work out how many are possible – not to find them all though, as there are over 700!

Checkpoints

Stop the class after a short period of time to discuss the initial approaches they have made. Find out if they have a structure or procedure for finding the times from earliest to latest, i.e. do they put the lowest number as the hour first then make the smallest number from the other two digits? See what suggestions they are thinking up for the stories. Highlight the unusual or inventive ones.

 ### Watch out for …

Children may use numbers higher than 5 in the tens position of the minutes number. Discuss with them why this is not possible. Children may simply make times without a thought for finding the earliest first. Point them in the right direction. Encourage them to use counting on for finding the difference between the times if they aren't already.

 ### Ask …

- ❯ *Which of these numbers will give you the lowest hour?*
- ❯ *What would happen if you made this an a.m. time instead of a p.m., how would that change your order?*
- ❯ *What may you be doing at this time of day?*
- ❯ *Is that a sensible suggestion?*

 ### Listen for …

Listen for discussion about swapping numbers around to make new times, particularly for reasoning why certain times are not possible. If you hear this type of talk going on, stop the class and ask those you heard to explain their thinking.

 Moving on …

Invite a few groups to tell the whole class their stories. Discuss what makes the stories interesting or creative.

Where next?

- ❯ Use digit cards in this way to generate and order 3-, 4- or 5-digit numbers for mathematical stories.
- ❯ Use some of the stories to make up a line graph during a data handling session. This can be developed for science subjects.

What worked well? Were they confident with clock times, or is this an area that should be revisited? Was this activity helpful for reinforcing time and including thinking skills?

DEBRIEF

What's the time?

Name _____ Date _____

Make your times from the digit cards. Draw the hands and write the time.

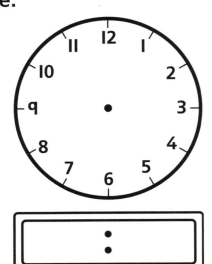

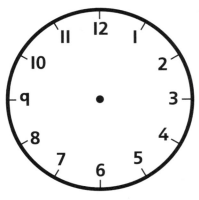

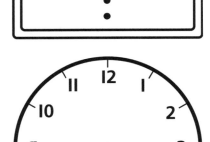

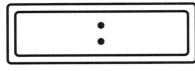

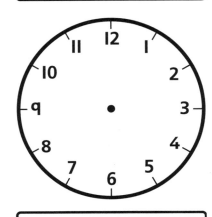

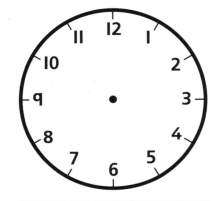

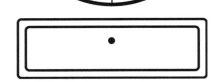

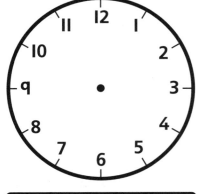

Cut out to make a pack of digit cards.

9	8	7
6	5	4
3	2	1
0	:	0

Fraction time!

In 'Fraction time!' the children are asked to use an analogue clock to make fractions. They will be making as many different fractions as they can and looking at their equivalences. The purpose of this activity is to develop their existing mathematical knowledge by practical and creative exploration which involves imagination, lateral thinking and extension.

Key maths links

- Recognize the equivalence of simple fractions
- Order simple fractions
- Relate fractions to division and find simple fractions of quantities
- Making decisions

Thinking skills

- Generate and extend ideas
- Visualize
- Look for alternatives

Language

minutes, analogue, fraction, equivalent, $\frac{1}{2}$, $\frac{1}{3}$, $\frac{2}{3}$, $\frac{1}{4}$, $\frac{3}{4}$, $\frac{1}{6}$, $\frac{2}{6}$ etc., visualize, suppose, alternative

Resources

PCM 15 (three per pair and enlarged copy)
PCM 16 (one per pair)
copy of clock (cut into half, one quarter and one sixth)
paper
pencils and pens
scissors
glue

Setting the scene

Ask the children to find some fractions of numbers, e.g. $\frac{1}{4}$ of 20, $\frac{3}{4}$ of 20, $\frac{1}{3}$ of 30, $\frac{2}{3}$ of 30 and show you, using digit cards or whiteboards. Discuss how to find $\frac{3}{4}$ of a number from their knowledge of $\frac{1}{4}$.

Show an enlarged version of a clock from PCM 15. Cover it with a cut-out half. Ask what fraction is covered, move the half into different places so that the children can recognize that it is half, no matter where it is placed. Ask how many minutes are covered. Repeat this with the quarter. Place the half and the quarter on the clock and discuss $\frac{3}{4}$ and what it is equivalent to, e.g. $\frac{1}{2}$ plus $\frac{1}{4}$. Next, place the sixth on the clock, ask how many minutes are covered, what fraction of the hour that is and how they know.

Getting started

The children should work in pairs. Each pair will need three copies of PCM 15, scissors, glue and a large piece of paper. Their task is to cut the clock faces into as many different unit fraction parts as they can, work out what fractions they have made and their values in minutes. They need to stick their fraction parts onto a large piece of paper and label them in fractions and in minutes. They should then order them from smallest to largest on a number line from PCM 16. Encourage them to be creative and explorative with their fraction pieces by putting two or more together to make new fractions that they haven't used in class before.

Simplify

Initially, keep one clock whole and encourage the children to cut the other into half and a quarter and explore how many ways they can place these on the whole clock to give the same fraction. Encourage them to look at the relationship between wholes, halves, quarters and three quarters. When they are confident with this ask them to explore other fractions which can be grouped, i.e. thirds and sixths.

Challenge

After they have finished the original task, they should cut more clock faces into unit fraction parts and put them together to see how many equivalent fractions they can make (therefore moving away from unit fractions) and list these, e.g. $\frac{1}{3}$ (20 minutes) = $\frac{2}{6}$ (2 × 10 minutes) = $\frac{4}{12}$ (4 × 5 minutes) = $\frac{8}{24}$ (8 × 2$\frac{1}{2}$ minutes); $\frac{1}{2}$ (30 minutes) = $\frac{4}{8}$ (4 × 7$\frac{1}{2}$ minutes) = $\frac{5}{10}$ (5 × 6 minutes) = $\frac{2}{4}$ (2 × 15 minutes). The use of colour for different fractions can enhance this activity.

Checkpoints

This task will need monitoring to ensure that the children are exploring unfamiliar fractions as well as ones they know, e.g. 6ths, 12ths, 30ths. Bring the class together for a mini-plenary; offering 'opt out' points for those that are confident. Discuss which fractions have been made so far. Find out if they have a method for finding them or if they are working randomly. Encourage them to look at fractions that can be made and which will give half numbers of minutes.

Watch out for ...

Some children may not be able to figure out which fraction they have made, encourage them to move the fraction around a whole clock face to see how many times it will fit. Explain that the number of times the part fits indicates the fraction denominator.

Ask ...

- ◗ *How many ways can you make half an hour using the fraction parts you have cut out?*
- ◗ *What could you add to make 45 minutes?*
- ◗ *Can you demonstrate and explain what you have just done?*
- ◗ *Can you think of a question to ask?*

Listen for ...

Some children may start to see patterns which involve doubling and halving, for example to make new fractions. Some children may be very creative in their ability to use the fraction parts to make other fractions, ask them to share their ideas.

 Moving on ...

List all the fractions the class have made on the board. Ask a few to show the ones they made. Ask the class to pick out those that are equivalent. See if they can suggest any that they have missed or think of strategies to create further equivalent fractions. Next, order them on a number line from 0 to 1.

Where next?

- ◗ Repeat this for mixed and improper fractions.
- ◗ Use this strategy in a lesson on time.

How confident were the children at identifying fractions? Did the activity highlight weaknesses and strengths? Were there sufficient elements of creativity in this session? How could this aspect be improved another time?

DEBRIEF

Cut out one clock face to make fractions.

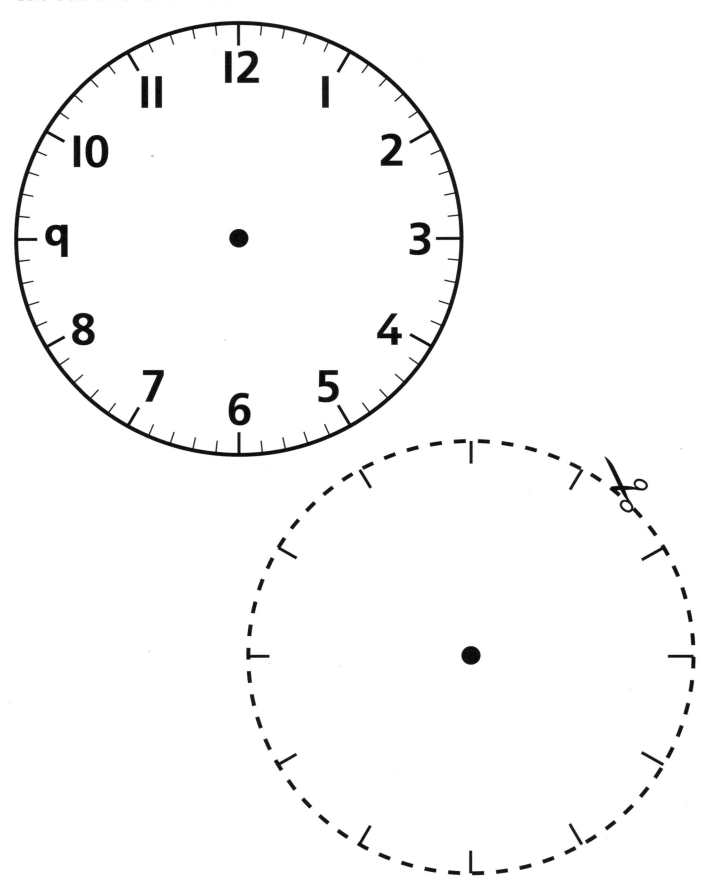

Number lines

Use the number lines to order your fractions.

Assessing progress

Assessing the development of creative thinking is challenging as there are often a number of solutions and ideas that can be considered creative in any particular situation. You will have to consider the individual pupil too. A genuinely creative thought for one pupil – something new and insightful for them – may not be so creative in another. Also the process is not necessarily regular or frequent. It is therefore important to consider children's attitudes or their dispositions in different situations. They should be asking questions and be confident to offer ideas. It is this confidence or perhaps playfulness that is the best indicator of creativity, rather than trying to assess specific solutions or outcomes.

Cross-curricular thinking

Literacy

Brainstorming for ideas is a good general technique to develop creative thinking. It is important that it is done in an atmosphere where the children know that offering ideas is more important than coming up with the right answer and where all ideas are accepted uncritically. In literacy this technique can be used when responding to a text to record thoughts and feelings, as well as to stimulate ideas for composition in terms of the content and detail of the vocabulary used. Brainstorming is usually conducted as a whole class activity. It can also be useful to start off in groups so that the children become more independent in using the technique.

Science

Using analogies can be a powerful way to develop scientific understanding in a creative way. Asking children to think of an analogy for something (such as an electric current being like water pipes with the current flowing round a circuit) not only provides an opportunity to compare why they are alike and how they are not alike, but also offers an insight into children's thinking about the science involved.

Design Technology

Coming up with ideas is an essential part of the design process. One technique that can help is to ask children to visualize how the product will be used. Ask them to 'see' it once it is finished: *What will it need to do?, What will make your idea different or special?* This can be the basis for more structured planning and development, though the whole process is a creative one.

Geography

The strategy 'Banned' (where an idea or object is described without using certain banned words) can easily be developed in other subjects and provides opportunities to develop specific vocabulary. However, it can also be a way to stimulate creative thinking as children will come up with imaginative ways to give clues to words, such as: *It sounds like fountain but starts with an 'm'.* They may find it hard to formulate rules for banned ideas or words. It is usually best to praise their ingenuity and finish with a discussion of creative ways to get round the rules.

In my opinion ...

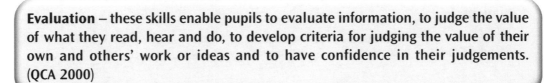

Evaluation skills

> **Evaluation** – these skills enable pupils to evaluate information, to judge the value of what they read, hear and do, to develop criteria for judging the value of their own and others' work or ideas and to have confidence in their judgements. (QCA 2000)

Overview

Evaluation is about taking responsibility for your own opinions and judgements and being prepared to explain or defend them to others with reasons. It requires confidence in knowing what you think and sensitivity in evaluating or criticizing the work of others. It requires the ability to set and apply criteria to tasks and make judgements based on those criteria. The final stage is presenting these judgements to others and being prepared to defend or change that judgement in the light of feedback. This involves awareness of the feelings of others in giving and receiving feedback – a challenging aspect of effective collaboration and an important aspect of speaking and listening.

In mathematics evaluation is essential in developing confidence in knowing that you have a good solution and understanding why. Mathematics is often perceived as being about applying rules or being able to remember facts and formulas. However, an essential part of being able to think mathematically is to be able to make judgements about which facts to use or which formula to apply. A good solution in mathematics might be an efficient one, or an elegant one, or one that leads to new insights and thinking. Deciding which is the best way to do something mathematically therefore, often calls for evaluation and judgement.

Strategies

Evaluation skills can be broken down further into the following kinds of behaviours or activities that pupils can do:

- ◗ **Evaluate information**
  Appraise, assess, critique, decide
- ◗ **Judge the value of what they read, hear and do**
  Review, weigh up, scrutinize
- ◗ **Develop criteria for judging the value of their own and others' work or ideas**
  Evaluate, judge, mark
- ◗ **Being confident in their judgements**
  Express opinions, disagree, agree (with reasons), resolve

Questions

How could you justify that? What reasons are important? Can you explain ...? How will you check it? Can you argue the opposite? Do you agree? Do you disagree? Which do you think?

Good buy?

BRIEF

In 'Good buy?' the children are asked to design an outfit with accessories to fit certain criteria, one of which is a financial constraint. This activity encourages the children to evaluate information and make decisions from it and then justify them to a partner, whilst in turn evaluating their partner's justifications. It also makes use of number skills, particularly addition and subtraction in 'real life' situations.

Key maths links

- Making decisions
- Problems involving 'real life' with money
- Addition and subtraction

Thinking skills

- Decision making
- Justification
- Expression of opinions

Language

total, change, agree, disagree, opinion, reason, decide

Resources

PCM 17 (cut out and attached to the pictures of clothing)
PCM 18 (one per pair)
pictures of a variety of children's/young adult's clothes, footwear and accessories
paper
pencils and pens
scissors
glue

Setting the scene

Show the children a selection of the catalogue pictures and ask them to choose some that they would like to wear. Pin up their choices. Ask the children to total the cost of pairs of clothes and then a whole outfit. Expect them to explain how they worked out these calculations. Tell the children that they have a starting amount, say, £50, and ask them to work out what change they have.

Getting started

The children should work in pairs within a group of four to six. Each group will need a selection of pictures of clothes cut out from a catalogue or printed from an online store. They should include party outfits, sports wear, casual and smart clothing for summer and winter wear. Each item of clothing should be priced. As a pair, they take it in turns to pick a card from PCM 18 and make up a 4-piece outfit that best fits the criteria. They should pick a top or jacket, something to cover their legs (trousers, jeans, skirt etc.), footwear and an accessory. Then they work out the cost of the outfit and how much they have left and agree a justification they can present to the rest of their group. The group provides feedback to each of the pairs.

Simplify

Encourage the children to choose two or three items only. Instead of criteria cards, give them a budget of £20 and ask them to make up their own criteria, which can be a simple as: *I chose these because I like the colour and they both come to £15, so I'll get some change.*

Challenge

As well as justifying their choices against the given criteria, ask the children to design their own clothes and make up their own prices that will suit the criteria.

Checkpoints

It is important to encourage children to listen to each other and be supportive. Watch out for children who work well together and let the class know this is what you are looking for. Stop the class occasionally and highlight those children who are effective at supporting good evaluation.

Watch out for ...

Evaluating can be rather negative, so encourage the children to make positive contributions, finding at least one decision that they agree with! Ensure they are accurate with their calculations and don't spend all their time talking about their choices and so neglecting the maths.

Ask ...

- ◉ *How could you justify that choice?*
- ◉ *Do you agree or disagree? Why?*
- ◉ *Would you have chosen differently? Why?*
- ◉ *What reasons are the most important?*

Listen for ...

Some children may have very creative justifications: invite them to share their ideas with the class. You may hear some children disagreeing: find out if their view is appropriate or if they are simply disagreeing for the sake of it!

 ## Moving on ...

Ask the children to make a poster by selecting one of their choices and sticking the clothes, labels and criteria onto paper. Invite pairs of children to share their work with the rest of the class by reading the criteria statement, showing the poster and explaining why they made their choices. They should also total prices and work out how much money they were left with, using sensible and efficient mathematical strategies. Finally their partner should explain why they agreed or disagreed with the choice.

Where next?

- ◉ This kind of activity could be taken into science, when the children discuss such things as electrical dangers in the home, growth conditions for plants, healthy foods.
- ◉ Try a discussion regarding different landscapes and their suitability for different uses.
- ◉ The procedure can be used in the justification of preferences on artists and their work.

How confident were the children at justifying their choices? Did the activity highlight weaknesses and strengths in terms of evaluation skills? Did the idea of creating their own outfits inspire any children who at other times are reluctant mathematicians? Can you see a way to introduce this kind of approach into other maths lessons?

DEBRIEF

Money labels

Cut out and place on clothing.

50p	75p	99p	£1
£1·50	£1·75	£2·50	£3·99
£4·25	£5·98	£7·75	£9·99
£10	£12·50	£13·75	£14·99
£15·75	£15·99	£16	£16·90
£17·50	£18·99	£19·99	£20
£21·75	£22·50	£24·99	£25·50
£29·99	£34·50	£35	£39·99

Thinking by Numbers 4 • Unit 5: In my opinion ... • Evaluation skills

Criteria statements

Cut out the cards.
Work out the cost of each outfit and the change you will get.

a Billie-Jean has £50 to spend. She is going to play in a tennis tournament. She needs to be able to run easily and move her arms. She likes bright colours. Choose an outfit for her to wear.

b Samir and his friend Shaun are going to play in a football tournament. They have £80 to spend. They prefer designer type kit and smart football boots. Choose two outfits for them to wear.

c Georgia and Jack have £100 to spend. They are going on holiday to somewhere really hot. Make up two outfits for them to wear while they are sight-seeing.

d Apple and her friend have £100 to spend. They are going on holiday where they'll spend most of their time on the beach. They like swimming. Make up 2 outfits for them both to wear.

e Birch is going on a cycling holiday in France. He has £50 to spend and wants to look trendy. Make up an outfit for him to wear.

f Tom's mother has won a competition for him to go to see Santa in Lapland. She has £50 to spend. It will be very, very cold.

g You have £100 to spend. It's winter, it's cold and you have nothing to wear. Make up an outfit that you could buy.

h Sal has £100 to spend. It's springtime; it's wet and chilly. She has nothing to wear. She likes to dress really smart. Make up an outfit that she could buy.

i You have £50 to spend. It's summer, it's very hot and you have nothing to wear. Make up an outfit that you could buy.

j You have been invited to a wedding. You need some smart new clothes. You have £75 to spend. Make up an outfit that you could buy.

k You are going camping. You need some clothes to take with you. The weather forecast is for lots of rain. You have £100 to spend. Make up an outfit that you could buy.

l Shula is going to a party. She needs a new outfit. It needs to be as funky as possible. She has £50 to spend. Make up an outfit that she could buy.

m You have £100 to spend. You want to buy some clothes. You have to save at least £30 of your money. Make up an outfit that you could buy and would be proud to wear.

n Your sister wants a trendy outfit. She has £80 to spend. Make up an outfit for her to wear.

o Your brother wants a cool outfit. He has £80 to spend. Make up an outfit for him to wear.

Best fit?

In 'Best fit?' the children are asked to sort numbers into a Venn diagram according to given criteria. This activity encourages the children to evaluate information, through reasoning about numbers with particular reference to multiplication and division, then make a decision from their evaluations and justify their reasons.

Key maths links

- Making decisions
- Data handling
- Reasoning about numbers
- Multiplication and division

Thinking skills

- Decision making
- Justification
- Expression of opinions

Language

multiples, remainders, division, multiplication, agree, disagree, opinion, reason, decide

Resources

PCM 19 (one per pair)
PCM 20 (one per pair)
scissors

Setting the scene

Write a number on the board, such as 35. Ask the children to make division sentences using that number. Encourage them to come up with these: $35 \div 35 = 1$, $35 \div 1 = 35$, $35 \div 5 = 7$ and $35 \div 7 = 5$. Prompt explanations: *What do these sentences mean?* Ask them to talk to each other and try to come up with ideas for more sentences. After a few minutes bring the class together and invite suggestions. If necessary, prompt them to think about remainders: $70 \div 2 = 35$, $140 \div 35 = 4$, $35 \div 4 = 8$ remainder 3, $35 \div 10 = 3$ remainder 5. Now ask them to sort these sentences into categories and label the categories. Demonstrate using a Venn diagram and ask the class to think up good titles for the sets.

Getting started

Explain to the children that their task is to work in pairs to sort numbers according to multiples and remainders after a division. They need to select ten numbers from the pack (PCM 20) placed face down in front of them and sort them into a Venn diagram (PCM 19) according to the given criteria. There are two diagrams; choose which one you wish pairs of children to start with. They must place all their numbers in the diagram and write down in numbers on the PCM why they have placed them in a particular section. For example:

16 ($16 \div 4 = 4$),
14 ($14 \div 4 = 3$ r 2),
23 ($23 \div 3 = 7$ r 2)

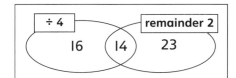

Simplify

Use a Venn diagram for one category, such as 'integers after being divided by 2'. The children should put all the even numbers in the diagram and the others outside and give the outside area a title, e.g. 'remainder 1'. This could be made more complex by increasing the divisor to, say, 3 or 4, where the outside title would be just 'remainders'. The children should work out what each remainder is, e.g. $10 \div 4 = 2$ remainder 2.

Challenge

After the initial task, ask the children to have a go at the second task on PCM 19 and then repeat the exercise but making up numbers and criteria of their own. One of the criteria must have something to do with remainders.

③ Checkpoints

Stop the class after a short period of time to discuss initial approaches. Have they noticed any useful methods to work out how to put numbers in the remainder section? What do they look for to fill in the intersection? Invite pairs of children to share their ideas.

Watch out for ...

It is important to encourage the children to listen to each other's explanations and say whether they agree or disagree. Highlight those children who are doing this. Once a method has been established the activity is quite straightforward. Any children who have not found the method may need prompting to use a systematic approach: *Would it help to list the multiples of four? What if you looked for numbers that are two more than a multiple of four? What about even numbers and odd numbers?*

Ask ...

- ❍ *What do you think would be special about the number you divide by to get a remainder of three?*
- ❍ *How would counting in multiples of six, seven, eight or nine help?*
- ❍ *How could you justify that decision?*
- ❍ *Do you agree or disagree? Why?*

Listen for ...

Observe the children as they talk, listening for appropriate vocabulary such as multiple, divisor, remainder, my reasons are ... Listen for concise and accurate reasoning. Encourage the 'listening' partner to question the one explaining.

④ Moving on ...

As a whole class, go through a selection of the numbers and ask the children to say where they would go in the Venn diagram and why. Ask the children to reflect on their talk, their understanding of numbers, what they know and how it can help them to undertake a similar activity with more proficiency.

Where next?

- ❍ Try sorting shapes according to their properties and then labelling the sets.
- ❍ Identifying criteria in science to sort materials according to their properties or to classify living things and evaluating the resulting categories lends itself to this procedure.
- ❍ Identifying criteria can be used in geography to sort landscapes, kinds of weather conditions, land uses etc. and evaluating the categories.

How confident were the children at justifying their choices? Did the activity highlight weaknesses and strengths in their knowledge and understanding of divisors and multiples? How could you use this kind of approach into other maths calculation lessons?

DEBRIEF

Where does it go?

Name _____ **Date** _____

Place your numbers in the Venn diagram. Show your workings.

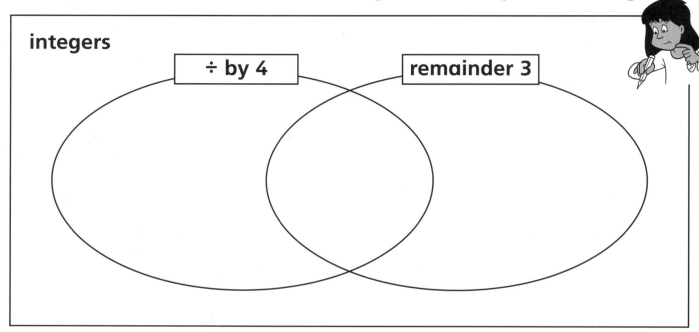

integers

÷ by 4   remainder 3

workings

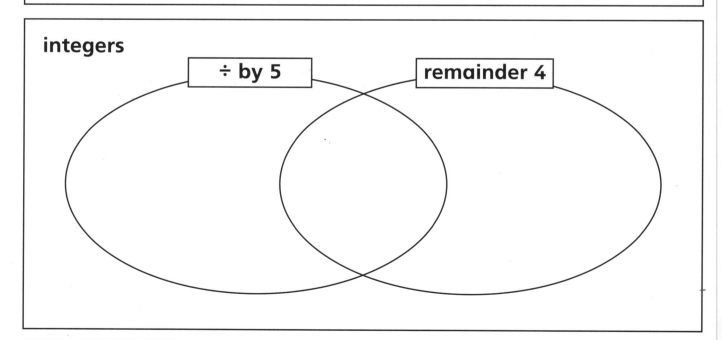

integers

÷ by 5   remainder 4

workings

Number cards

Cut out to make a pack of number cards.

7	8	15	17
18	21	23	24
29	30	32	35
38	42	44	45
49	52	56	58

Assessing progress

The children's increased confidence in their own thinking is one of the hallmarks of improving evaluation skills. It is about taking responsibility for your own opinions and judgements and being prepared to explain or defend them to others with reasons. This requires confidence in knowing what you think. This confidence should be justified, of course, so children should be prepared to change their minds if necessary, in the light of information or reasoning. At this stage it is also important for children to show sensitivity in evaluating or criticizing the work of others.

Cross-curricular thinking

Literacy

Assessment for learning (see page 14) strategies such as 'Traffic lights' are good starting points to develop evaluation skills. You can ask the children to rate a piece of writing that they have done with green for: *I think I can go on*, orange for: *I think I am getting going*, and red for: *I'm at a full stop here*. This opens up the way to discuss criteria for success in the task so that children can evaluate their own work.

Design technology

Evaluation is also central to design technology. The children need to learn to develop evaluation criteria for their designs in order to guide their thinking as they work. This should be an integral part of the process and not simply a retrospective review. Using a digital camera to record the process of designing and making enables the children to recall what they were thinking at the different stages and reflect on the criteria to evaluate the task.

History

A strategy such as a 'Mystery' (see page 23) can help children to use their evaluative skills as they judge the importance of the different 'clues' they have been given. In history this can be a good way to assess understanding of what has been learned in a unit of work as they use their historical knowledge to do this. Clues can easily be written to support a discussion about: *Who was responsible for the Great Fire of London?* for example, to get children to see that the baker may have started the fire, but that there are other factors to consider.

Geography

Some other general techniques that are helpful in developing evaluation skills are those developed by Edward deBono where children are given thinking frames with headings such as 'Plus, minus and interesting' (PMI) (see page 23) or a focus on 'Consider all factors' (CAF). The structure of the sheet helps children to think more carefully and give more considered responses. These approaches can be combined with collaborative discussion (such as 'Think, Ink, Pair, Share' where children are asked to consider their response, make some notes, discuss it with a partner then in a group). This can be particularly useful in a subject like geography when the children have to evaluate changes to the environment or express their views about people and places.

Think on!
Using and applying thinking skills

> **Using and applying thinking** – in mathematics these skills involve pupils in developing the skills and strategies that will help them solve problems they face both in learning at school and in life more broadly. They involve problem solving in its broadest sense and include the skills of identifying and understanding what the issue or the problem is, planning solutions, monitoring progress in tackling the issue or problem and then reviewing and evaluating any solutions.

Overview

The aim of this unit is to identify some activities for pupils to put their mathematical thinking skills into practice. This will give them the opportunity to evaluate how well they have developed their skills through the earlier activities as well as giving you the opportunity to assess how well they can apply what they have learned. The activities are set as challenges, problems or puzzles.

The process of undertaking these activities relates to the different kinds of thinking in the earlier units. The early stages draw on information processing skills by focusing the children on what they have to do and what they already know. There may be scope for creativity in seeing alternatives or applying knowledge and skills imaginatively to a new problem. Enquiry skills are brought into play during the main part of the activity as any solution is formulated and tested, closely supported by reasoning skills which also help to link the different stages and ensure continuity throughout the process. Evaluation skills are essential to appraise and review any solution and to develop confidence in being successful.

Strategies

Supporting the pupils in using and applying thinking skills to problems is best framed as a series of questions:

- **What do we have to do?**
  What is the problem, challenge or issue to be resolved?
- **Where do we start?**
  What do we know?
  Have we done anything like this before?
  What possibilities are there?
- **How will we know when we have got there?**
  What will a successful solution look like?
- **Are we on track?**
  Is this going to lead us to the answer we imagined?
- **Have we got there?**
  Is this a solution to the problem we were set?
  Could we have done it differently? Is it the best solution?

Questions

What do you have to do? What do you need to know? What do you know already? Have you seen anything like this before? What could you try? Do you think that will work? What will the answer look like? How could you test that? How can you check that? Is this the best answer? How else could you have done it?

Sweetie dilemma

The 'Sweetie dilemma' activity encourages the children to use and apply the maths they know to solve a problem – a kind of living graph. They will have to use problem solving skills to monitor their progress and check the reasonableness of their solutions then identify any mistakes or if they have been inefficient in their approach. The activity will give you the opportunity to assess these aspects of their thinking.

Key maths links

- 'Real life' problems involving measures
- Data handling
- Reasoning about numbers
- Know equivalences between g and kg

Thinking skills

- Using and applying
- Problem solving

Language

gram, kilogram, difference, altogether, convert, equivalent, problem, solution, calculation, strategy, decide

Resources

PCM 21 (one per pair and one enlarged)
PCM 22 (one per pair)

 Setting the scene

Introduce the problem using a brief story about Mr Smith and his sweet shop along the lines of: *Mr Smith is in a bit of a dilemma. He has a computer which makes up charts and graphs to show the weights of each type of sweet he has in stock in his shop. These help him to know when he is running short of any sweets and so needs to reorder them. He switched on his computer this morning and this is what he saw.* Show an enlarged version of the graph on PCM 21. Ask the children to tell you as much information from it as they can. Then ask them why Mr Smith has a problem. Discuss what information is missing.

Getting started

The children work in pairs using the information on PCM 22 to work out which sweets match each bar on the graph on PCM 21 (this indicates a particular weight). As a class, they need to begin by answering the following questions: *What do we have to find out? What do we have to do? What do we know already? Where do we start?* Discuss each question in detail.

Simplify

Use the simpler set of clues at the bottom of PCM 22. Cut them out so that the children are able to sort them into those that can be grouped together because they are related to each other.

Challenge

After they have completed the initial task, ask the children to evaluate what they did and see if they can find other ways of solving the problem and decide if they are efficient. Next, ask them to make up their own dilemma. They need to make up an appropriate bar graph and clues to enable the dilemma to be solved. Once they have done this they can give it to another pair to answer. They may need some support for this.

Checkpoints

After a short while, gather the class together for a mini-plenary to discuss how the children are getting on. Check to see if they have been able to identify useful information and find out how they can use it to work out the weight of some of the sweets. If any pairs need extra input from you, keep them with you and guide them as suggested in 'Watch out for...'. Offer opt-out points for those that are confident and want to get on.

Watch out for ...

If children have difficulty starting, suggest that they group the clues. One way to start is to find the clues with same sweet names. Get them to cut out the clues so that they can move them around. Then the children can begin comparing them. Once they have done this encourage them to find out which ones can be worked out first.

Look for children who are discussing this successfully and ask them to feed back to the class with their ideas.

Ask ...

- *What do you know already?*
- *What clues could you focus on first? Why?*
- *Are these going to lead to a solution? Why?*
- *Do you think you will need to use all the clues?*

Listen for ...

Listen for reasons about why they are using certain clues and how they work things out. If you hear this, stop the class and ask those you heard to explain their thinking.

 Moving on ...

Go through the clues, asking the children to group the ones that are useful and explain why. Work through the clues, asking specific children to explain how they used them. Invite others to give alternative methods, if appropriate. When each solution is arrived at, encourage the children to explain how it will help lead to an answer for the problem set.

Where next?

- This kind of method can be adapted to other areas of measures: capacity, length and time.
- Use a similar type of exercise for a shape dilemma.
- Apply the procedure to foundation subjects, such as history and ordering events in time.

How confident were the children at starting out in this activity? In order to begin, were they able to sort through the clues to find those they needed with ease? Did you feel that you gave enough or too much direction? Did any of the children surprise you in the logical way that they approached this task? How could you use this kind of approach in other areas of maths?

DEBRIEF

Mr Smith's dilemma

Help Mr Smith sort out his sweets.

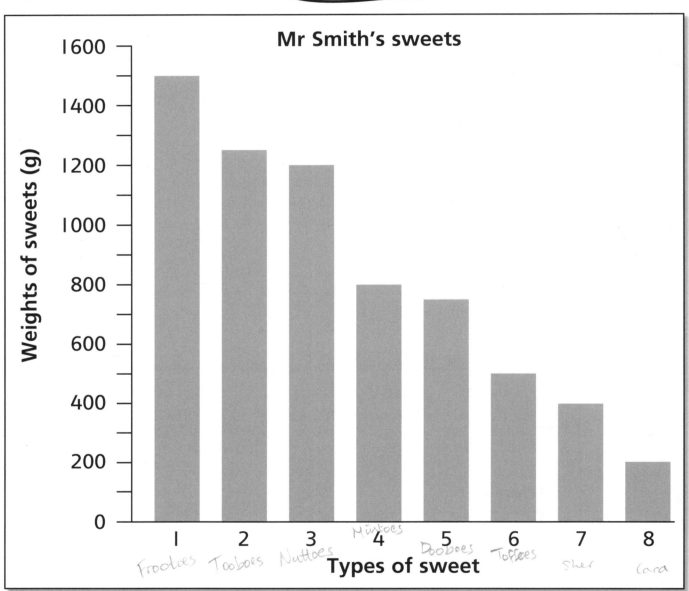

Mr Smith's sweets

Weights of sweets (g): 0, 200, 400, 600, 800, 1000, 1200, 1400, 1600

Types of sweet: 1, 2, 3, 4, 5, 6, 7, 8

Frootoes Tooboes Nuttoes Mintoes Dooboes Toffoes Sher Cara

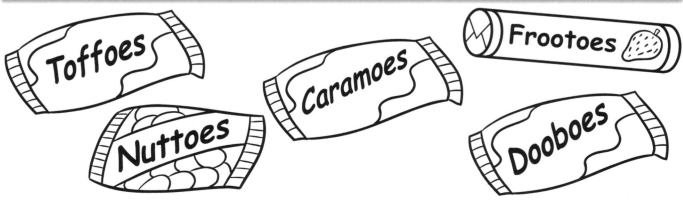

From these clues work out what weight of each type of sweet Mr Smith has.

Tooboes are heavier than Nuttoes	Nuttoes are lighter than Frootoes
The difference in weight between the Toffoes and the Sherboes is 100 g	The Nuttoes and Frootoes weigh over 2·5 kg together
Altogether the Mintoes and Caramoes weigh 1 kg	The Dooboes are 550 g heavier than the Caramoes
The Caramoes are half the weight of the Sherboes	

What is the weight of each type of sweet in Mr Smith's shop? Cut out and group the clues to help you.

The Caramoes are the lightest	The Sherboes are twice the weight of the Caramoes
The Frootoes are the heaviest	The Nuttoes and Frootoes weigh over 2·5 kg together
Tooboes are heavier than Nuttoes	Altogether the Mintoes and Caramoes weigh 1 kg
The Dooboes are 50 g lighter than the Mintoes	The difference in weight between the Toffoes and the Sherboes is 100 g

Money, money, money!

BRIEF

In 'Money, money, money' the children use their problem solving skills to work through a task to a conclusion. The children need to identify relevant information and decide on a system to find all possible solutions. They also use and apply the addition and subtraction strategies they know and look for rules and patterns to find these solutions.

Key maths links

- 'Real-life' problems involving money
- Convert pounds to pence
- Addition and subtraction
- Reasoning about numbers

Thinking skills

- Using and applying
- Problem solving

Language

pounds, pence, difference, altogether, convert, problem, solution, calculation, strategy, decide

Resources

PCM 23 (one per pair)
PCM 24 (one per child)
coins

Setting the scene

Write an amount of mixed pounds and pence on the board, such as £4·50. Ask the children for as many ways as they can think of to make that amount of money. List ten of their suggestions on the board. If they haven't suggested these, ask them to think of the following: the most coins, the least coins, silver coloured coins only, coins that are valued at over 20p. Then ask: *A CD costs £4·50. I have a £10 note; the shopkeeper gave me six coins as change. What coins could he have given me?* Expect all the possibilities. Repeat this with a different number of coins, say ten, as change.

Getting started

The children work in pairs to solve the problem on PCM 23. Read it through with the class and explain that their task is to find all the combinations of coins that Fred could use to answer the question. They need to begin by thinking: *What is the question asking? What do we have to find out? What do we know already? What can we do with that information? Where do we start?* Encourage them to use efficient strategies and to be systematic in their approach to find all possibilities: Will they start by using the smallest coins or the largest? Will they control variables one at a time such as by starting with a 50p then working out all possibilities for this. They also need to find an efficient method of recording. A grid is the most systematic though a spider diagram for each coin can be very effective.

Once the children have successfully completed Fred's problem direct them to Samantha's problem on PCM 23.

Simplify

Give the children a definite number of possibilities to find at first. You may like to alter the number of coins in Fred's pocket, e.g. four 50ps, three 20ps, one 2p; alternatively, alter the cost of the book.

Challenge

Alter the amounts, e.g. the cost of the book to £7·95 and the number of coins to three 50ps, three 20ps, seven 5ps, thirteen 2ps. Ask some 'What if ...' questions, e.g. *What if the cost of the book doubled, went up by 10% or was reduced by $\frac{1}{4}$, how would that change your answer?*

Ask the children to make up some similar problems to ask the whole class later.

Checkpoints

Gather the class together for a mini-plenary to discuss progress. Invite a few pairs to show their methods of recording. Ask the class to make a quick evaluation: are these efficient or can they think of a better way? Sit with groups of pairs and watch to see how they are finding all the possibilities. Encourage more systematic ways of working.

Watch out for ...

Provide coins for children who have difficulty starting, but encourage them not to be dependent on them. Stop the class briefly if you spot any children that have a systematic approach, and ask them to share their ideas.

Ask ...

- ❍ *What do you know already?*
- ❍ *How are you going to start?*
- ❍ *What are the fewest coins which will make the difference?*
- ❍ *Can you use two types of coin only, three types of coin?*

Listen for ...

Highlight effective and efficient strategies as well as examples of good collaboration to the rest of the class as an example of what you would like to see.

 Moving on ...

Make a list of all the possibilities on the board with the class. Introduce a few 'What if ...?' questions as suggested in the 'Challenge'. See if the children can make links, i.e. that if the book price is doubled, Fred will need double the amount he originally needed. Invite the children who made up their own problems to ask the class to solve them.

Where next?

- ❍ This can be adapted to shape problems, particularly when thinking about numbers of sides in 2D and faces in 3D.
- ❍ Developing and evaluating ways of recording is a crucial skill in both science and mathematics.

How confident were the children at recording their work in an efficient way? Would more input into this be appropriate? Did the children work systematically, using a constant each time and working through all the possibilities with that coin first then moving on? How did they respond to your 'What if ...?' questions? Could they make links and adapt their work accordingly or do you feel more input is needed here?

DEBRIEF

What coins are needed?

2

Fred has the following in his pocket:
one 50p, one 20p, one 10p,
two 5ps, four 2ps and three 1ps.
How much money does he have?
He wants to buy a book. It costs £4·50.
How much more does he need?
What coins could he have to make up
the difference?

£4·50

1

Samantha has the following in her bag:
one pound coin, two 50ps, one 20p,
two 10ps, four 5ps and three 2ps and
a penny.
How much money does she have?
She wants to buy a CD single. It costs
£3·99.
How much more does she need?
What coins could she have to make up
the difference?

£3·99

My recording sheet

Name _____ **Date** _____

Show your workings for the coins needed.

Thinking by Numbers 4 • **Unit 6: Think on!** • **Using and applying thinking skills**

What's my angle?

BRIEF

The activity 'What's my angle' makes use of the knowledge Year 4 children have of angles and develops the skills of using and applying this knowledge to all shapes. The children will solve a problem which entails recognizing and explaining patterns and relationships as well as generalizing and predicting. They will use their knowledge of how to tackle a problem, including which questions to ask to get started, identifying relevant information and strategies to reach a conclusion.

Key maths links

- Shape
- Angles
- Problem solving

Thinking skills

- Using and applying
- Problem solving

Language

triangle, equilateral triangle, isosceles triangle, quadrilateral, rectangle, square, pentagon, hexagon, heptagon, octagon, polygon

Resources

PCM 25 (one per pair)
PCM 26 (one per pair)
calculators

1 Setting the scene

Recap what has already been learnt about angles in numeracy lessons. Ask the children to tell you all they know. Expect the following:

- they are measured in degrees
- one whole turn is 360° or four right angles
- a quarter turn is 90° or one right angle
- half a right angle is 45°
- each angle at the corners of all rectangles and squares is 90°
- each angle of an equilateral triangle is 60°.

Recap the names and properties of the polygons (any regular or irregular shape that has three sides or more) that the children should know.

2 Getting started

Ask some 'prompt' questions to remind them of things they already know, such as: *What is the total of the angles in a rectangle?* (360°) *How about a triangle?* (180°) Next, ask them to think about the relationship between a triangle and a rectangle. Ask them to work with a partner and take feedback. If appropriate, show that you can put two triangles together to make a rectangle:

Ask them to make some sketches to see if this is the same for any quadrilateral. Then, give the children PCM 25 where they can make two triangles out of the quadrilaterals. Explain that if they know the total of the angles in a triangle they can find the total of the angles in a pentagon, and so on, once they have found the number of triangles in it.

Simplify

Give the children PCM 26, which has shapes already drawn for them to use.

Challenge

After the initial task, ask the children to find the total size of angles in a decagon and to come up with a general 'formula' that will enable them to work out the sum of the (interior) angles in any shape. Once they have figured one out, ask them to try it with a fifteen-sided shape, twenty-sided shape and even a 100-sided shape. Expect them to use a calculator for the working out and also to check. A table to record their findings may help them to generalize. See if they notice that the number of triangles inside a regular polygon is 2 less than the number of sides so in a 100-sided shape will be $98 \times 180°$!

Checkpoints

Ask the class if they were able to find the total of the interior angles of a pentagon. Invite someone to demonstrate their answer. For those that are working confidently, give an opt-out point so that they can continue with the task. For those that need some extra input, discuss in more detail and with more illustrations, that a quadrilateral can be made from two triangles so the sum of its interior angles would be $180° \times 2$ which is $360°$. Repeat for the pentagon showing that it can be made from three triangles, so its total angle size would be $180° \times 3$. Remind them that calculators are available.

Watch out for ...

Some of the children may be dividing their shape incorrectly and creating too many small triangles. It is important that they go from one corner of the shape to the other without crossing. Crossing joins all of the vertices in the shape.

 ✓   ✗

Ask ...

- ❍ *What do you know that can help solve the problem?*
- ❍ *Is this going to lead you to an answer?*
- ❍ *How can making a diagram help?*
- ❍ *If you know that works for two hexagons, will it work for all? Why?*

Listen for ...

Some children may see patterns and generalizations fairly quickly. If this is the case, stop the class and ask them to share what they can 'see'.

Moving on ...

Investigate if this works for irregular polygons. Challenge them to draw an irregular polygon that it would not work for.

Where next?

- ❍ *How many sides will a shape have if the sum of its interior angles is $1080°$?*
- ❍ *Investigate the area of triangles by working out the area of rectangles and halving.*

What worked well in this activity? Did the children use their knowledge of shape and angles confidently? Did any come up with generalizations? Could you bring generalizing into other areas of mathematics to reinforce this?

DEBRIEF

What's my angle?

Name _____ Date _____

Can you make each of these quadrilaterals into two triangles? Draw the lines to show this.

| total of angles = ___° | total of angles = ___° | total of angles = ___° | total of angles = ___° |

Work out the total of the angles. Draw one regular and one irregular form of these shapes.

1 Pentagon

| total of angles = ___° | total of angles = ___° |

2 Hexagon

| total of angles = ___° | total of angles = ___° |

3 Heptagon

| total of angles = ___° | total of angles = ___° |

4 Octagon

| total of angles = ___° | total of angles = ___° |

Can you make up a rule?

Use it to find the total of the angles in a 10-sided shape.

Totalling the angles

Name _____ Date _____

Can you make each of these quadrilaterals into two triangles?
Draw the lines to show this.

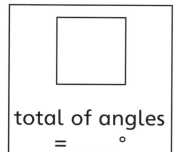

total of angles
= ____°

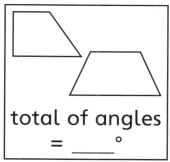

total of angles
= ____°

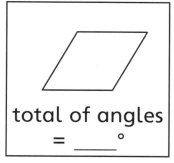

total of angles
= ____°

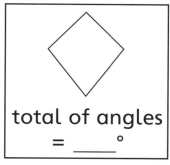

total of angles
= ____°

Draw triangles inside these shapes.

Use the information to work out the total of the angles in each shape.

1 Pentagon

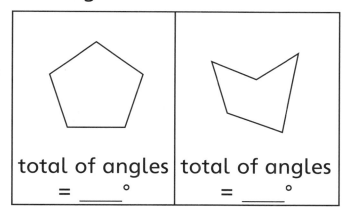

total of angles
= ____°

total of angles
= ____°

2 Hexagon

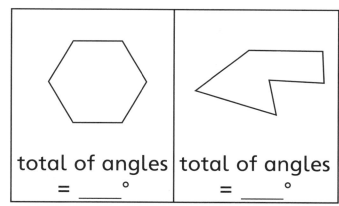

total of angles
= ____°

total of angles
= ____°

3 Heptagon

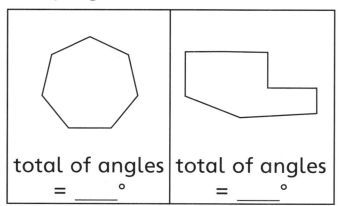

total of angles
= ____°

total of angles
= ____°

4 Octagon

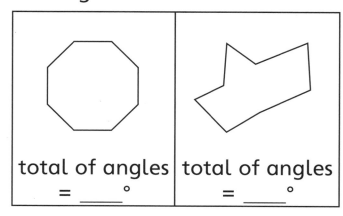

total of angles
= ____°

total of angles
= ____°

Summary

Assessing progress

The aim of this final unit was to offer some activities for pupils to put their mathematical thinking skills into practice. This should have given you the opportunity to evaluate how well they have developed their skills through the earlier activities as well as the opportunity to assess how well they can apply what they have learned. The grid below is a way for you to review where you think the children have made progress. It is designed for you to use on the whole class, but could be used to reflect on individual children. It is set out as a grid so that you can indicate where you think the first five units were successful, whether the children were able to show these skills in the activities in Unit 6, where you think you have seen progress in other areas of the curriculum, and where you think the children have developed their awareness of their thinking skills. You may wish to review the activities with a colleague who has also been using the *Thinking by Numbers* activities.

Thinking skills		Units 1–5	Unit 6, Using and applying	Across the curriculum	Awareness of the skills
Information processing	locate and collect relevant information				
	sort				
	classify				
	sequence				
	compare and contrast				
	analyse part/whole relationships				
Reasoning	give reasons for opinions and actions				
	draw inferences				
	make deductions				
	use precise language to explain what they think				
	make judgements and decisions informed by reasons or evidence				
Enquiry	ask relevant questions				
	pose and define problems				
	plan what to do and how to research				
	predict outcomes and anticipate consequences				
	test conclusions				
	improve ideas				
Creative thinking	generate and extend ideas				
	suggest hypotheses, to apply imagination				
	look for alternative innovative outcomes				
Evaluation	evaluate information				
	judge the value of what they read, hear and do				
	develop criteria for judging the value of their own and others' work or ideas				
	have confidence in their judgements				

Appendix

Scope and sequence chart

Unit	Unit name	Activity name	Key maths links	Thinking skills	Page no.
1	Sort it out! *Information processing skills*	Aliens ahoy!	▶ Properties of numbers ▶ Reasoning about numbers	▶ Sorting ▶ Classifying ▶ Comparing	26–29
		What do you need to know?	▶ Making decisions ▶ Reasoning about numbers ▶ Calculations ▶ Money	▶ Information processing ▶ Locate and classify relevant information ▶ Analyse relationships	30–33
2	That's because ... *Reasoning skills*	I can, I can't	▶ Properties of 2D shape	▶ Reasoning ▶ Draw inferences ▶ Make deductions ▶ Use of precise language ▶ Creativity	36–39
		Up the mountain	▶ Properties of number ▶ Place value ▶ Reasoning about numbers	▶ Give reasons for opinions ▶ Draw inferences ▶ Use precise language ▶ Make judgements	40–43
3	Detective work *Enquiry skills*	Who dunnit?	▶ Using ideas of simple proportion ▶ Length	▶ Enquiry ▶ Ask relevant questions ▶ Pose and define problems ▶ Predict outcomes	46–49
		Mystery numbers	▶ Reasoning about numbers ▶ Making decisions ▶ Calculations: +, −, x, ÷	▶ Enquiry ▶ Ask relevant questions ▶ Predict outcomes ▶ Test conclusions	50–53
4	What if ...? *Creative thinking skills*	Tell me a story	▶ Read the time from an analogue clock and 12 hour digital to the nearest minute ▶ Use a.m. and p.m. and the notation 4:57 ▶ Reasoning about numbers ▶ Making decisions ▶ Place value	▶ Generate and extend ideas ▶ Suggest hypotheses ▶ Apply imagination	56–59
		Fraction time!	▶ Recognize the equivalence of simple fractions ▶ Order simple fractions ▶ Relate fractions to division and find simple fractions of quantities ▶ Making decisions	▶ Generate and extend ideas ▶ Visualize ▶ Look for alternatives	60–63
5	In my opinion ... *Evaluation skills*	Good buy?	▶ Making decisions ▶ Problems involving 'real life' with money ▶ Addition and subtraction	▶ Decision making ▶ Justification ▶ Expression of opinions	66–69
		Best fit?	▶ Making decisions ▶ Data handling ▶ Reasoning about numbers ▶ Multiplication and division	▶ Decision making ▶ Justification ▶ Expression of opinions	70–73
6	Think on! *Using and applying thinking skills*	Sweetie dilemma	▶ 'Real life' problems involving measures ▶ Data handling ▶ Reasoning about numbers ▶ Know equivalences between g and kg	▶ Using and applying ▶ Problem solving	76–79
		Money, money, money!	▶ 'Real life' problems involving money ▶ Convert pounds to pence ▶ Addition and subtraction ▶ Reasoning about numbers	▶ Using and applying ▶ Problem solving	80–83
		What's my angle?	▶ Shape ▶ Angles ▶ Problems solving	▶ Using and applying ▶ Problem solving	84–87

Thinking by Numbers 4 and the NNS Unit Plans

The following chart shows how the thinking activities could be used if following the teaching order suggested in the NNS Unit Plans. Choose an appropriate activity to suit your class.

Autumn Term				
		Thinking by Numbers		
Unit	**Unit topic**	**Activity name**	**Thinking skill**	**Page no.**
1	Place value	Unit 2: Up the mountain Unit 4: Tell me a story	Reasoning Creative thinking	40–43 56–59
2	Addition and subtraction	Unit 1: What do you need to know? Unit 3: Mystery numbers Unit 5: Good buy? Unit 6: Money, money, money!	Information processing Enquiry Evaluation Using and applying	30–33 50–53 66–69 80–83
3	Addition and subtraction	Unit 1: What do you need to know? Unit 3: Mystery numbers Unit 5: Good buy? Unit 6: Money, money, money!	Information processing Enquiry Evaluation Using and applying	30–33 50–53 66–69 80–83
4	Reasoning about shape			
5	Length	Unit 3: Who dunnit?	Enquiry	46–49
6	Perimeter, coordinates	Unit 3: Who dunnit?	Enquiry	46–49
7	**Assess and review**			
8	Properties of numbers and number sequences Reasoning about numbers	Unit 1: Aliens ahoy! Unit 2: Up the mountain Unit 1: What do you need to know? Unit 3: Mystery numbers Unit 4: Tell me a story Unit 5: Best fit? Unit 6: Sweetie dilemma	Information processing Reasoning Information processing Enquiry Creative thinking Evaluation Using and applying	26–29 40–43 30–33 50–53 56–59 70–73 76–79
9	Multiplication and division	Unit 6: Money, money, money! Unit 1: What do you need to know? Unit 3: Mystery numbers Unit 4: Fraction time! Unit 5: Best fit?	Using and applying Information processing Enquiry Creative thinking Evaluation	80–83 30–33 50–53 60–63 70–73
10	Money and real-life problems	Unit 1: What do you need to know? Unit 5: Good buy? Unit 6: Money, money, money!	Information processing Evaluation Using and applying	30–33 66–69 80–83
11	Fractions, decimals	Unit 3: Who dunnit? Unit 4: Fraction time!	Enquiry Creative thinking	46–49 60–63
12	Addition and subtraction Time	Unit 1: What do you need to know? Unit 3: Mystery numbers Unit 5: Good buy? Unit 6: Money, money, money! Unit 4: Tell me a story	Information processing Enquiry Evaluation Using and applying Creative thinking	30–33 50–53 66–69 80–83 56–59
13	Handling data	Unit 5: Best fit? Unit 6: Sweetie dilemma	Evaluation Using and applying	70–73 76–79
14	**Assess and review**			

Spring Term				
		Thinking by Numbers		
Unit	**Unit topic**	**Activity name**	**Thinking skill**	**Page no.**
1	Ordering and rounding numbers			
2	Addition and subtraction	Unit 1: What do you need to know?	Information processing	30–33
		Unit 3: Mystery numbers	Enquiry	50–53
		Unit 5: Good buy?	Evaluation	66–69
		Unit 6: Money, money, money!	Using and applying	80–83
3	Written methods of addition and subtraction			
4	Measures – time, mass and area	Unit 4: Tell me a story	Creative thinking	56–59
		Unit 6: Sweetie dilemma	Using and applying	76–79
5	Problem solving	Unit 1: What do you need to know?	Information processing	30–33
		Unit 3: Mystery numbers	Enquiry	50–53
		Unit 6: Money, money, money!	Using and applying	80–83
6	Direction and angle	Unit 6: What's my angle?	Using and applying	84–87
7	**Assess and review**			
8	Properties of numbers and reasoning about numbers	Unit 1: Aliens ahoy!	Information processing	26–29
		Unit 1: What do you need to know?	Information processing	30–33
		Unit 2: Up the mountain	Reasoning	40–43
		Unit 3: Mystery numbers	Enquiry	50–53
		Unit 4: Tell me a story	Creative thinking	56–59
		Unit 5: Best fit?	Evaluation	70–73
		Unit 6: Sweetie dilemma	Using and applying	76–79
		Unit 6: Money, money, money!	Using and applying	80–83
9	Multiplication and division	Unit 1: What do you need to know?	Information processing	30–33
		Unit 3: Mystery numbers	Enquiry	50–53
		Unit 4: Fraction time!	Creative thinking	60–63
		Unit 5: Best fit?	Evaluation	70–73
10	Calculations and problem solving	Unit 1: What do you need to know?	Information processing	30–33
		Unit 3: Mystery numbers	Enquiry	50–53
		Unit 6: Money, money, money!	Using and applying	80–83
11	Fractions and decimals	Unit 3: Who dunnit?	Enquiry	46–49
		Unit 4: Fraction time!	Creative thinking	60–63
12	Handling data	Unit 5: Best fit?	Evaluation	70–73
		Unit 6: Sweetie dilemma	Using and applying	76–79
13	**Assess and review**			

Summer Term

Unit	Unit topic	Thinking by Numbers		
		Activity name	**Thinking skill**	**Page no.**
1	Place value	Unit 2: Up the mountain	Reasoning	40–43
		Unit 4: Tell me a story	Creative thinking	56–59
2	Addition and subtraction 1	Unit 1: What do you need to know?	Information processing	30–33
		Unit 3: Mystery numbers	Enquiry	50–53
		Unit 5: Good buy?	Evaluation	66–69
		Unit 6: Money, money, money!	Using and applying	80–83
3	Addition and subtraction 2	Unit 1: What do you need to know?	Information processing	30–33
		Unit 3: Mystery numbers	Enquiry	50–53
		Unit 5: Good buy?	Evaluation	66–69
		Unit 6: Money, money, money!	Using and applying	80–83
4	Measures	Unit 3: Who dunnit?	Enquiry	46–49
		Unit 4: Tell me a story	Creative thinking	56–59
		Unit 6: Sweetie dilemma	Using and applying	76–79
5	Shape and space	Unit 2: I can, I can't	Reasoning	36–39
6	Angles and position	Unit 6: What's my angle?	Using and applying	84–87
7	**Assess and review**			
8	Properties of number	Unit 1: Aliens ahoy!	Information processing	26–29
		Unit 2: Up the mountain	Reasoning	40–43
9	Multiplication and division 1	Unit 1: What do you need to know?	Information processing	30–33
		Unit 3: Mystery numbers	Enquiry	50–53
		Unit 4: Fraction time!	Creative thinking	60–63
		Unit 5: Best fit?	Evaluation	70–73
10	Multiplication and division 2	Unit 1: What do you need to know?	Information processing	30–33
		Unit 3: Mystery numbers	Enquiry	50–53
		Unit 4: Fraction time!	Creative thinking	60–63
		Unit 5: Best fit?	Evaluation	70–73
11	Fractions and decimals	Unit 3: Who dunnit?	Enquiry	46–49
		Unit 4: Fraction time!	Creative thinking	60–63
12	Addition and subtraction	Unit 1: What do you need to know?	Information processing	30–33
		Unit 3: Mystery numbers	Enquiry	50–53
		Unit 5: Good buy?	Evaluation	66–69
		Unit 6: Money, money, money!	Using and applying	80–83
13	Handling data	Unit 5: Best fit?	Evaluation	70–73
		Unit 6: Sweetie dilemma	Using and applying	76–79
14	**Assess and review**			

Thinking by Numbers 4 and the NNS Framework

Thinking skill	Unit	Activity name	Place value, ordering and rounding	Properties of numbers and number sequences	Fractions and decimals	Understanding addition and subtraction	Rapid recall of addition and subtraction facts	Mental calculation strategies (+ and −)	Paper and pencil procedures (+ and −)	Understanding multiplication and division	Rapid recall of multiplication and division facts	Mental calculation strategies (× and ÷)	Paper and pencil procedures (× and ÷)	Checking results of calculations	Making decisions	Reasoning about numbers and shapes	Problems involving 'real life', money or measures	Measures	Shape and space	Organizing and interpreting data
Information processing	1	Aliens ahoy!		✓												✓	-			
Information processing	1	What do you need to know?				✓	✓	✓		✓	✓	✓			✓	✓	✓			
Reasoning	2	I can, I can't		✓															✓	
Reasoning	2	Up the mountain	✓													✓				
Enquiry	3	Who dunnit?			✓	✓	✓	✓		✓	✓	✓			✓			✓		
Enquiry	3	Mystery numbers													✓	✓				
Creative thinking	4	Tell me a story	✓							✓	✓	✓			✓	✓		✓		
Creative thinking	4	Fraction time!			✓										✓					
Evaluation	5	Good buy?				✓	✓	✓		✓	✓	✓			✓	✓	✓			✓
Evaluation	5	Best fit?													✓	✓		✓		✓
Using and applying thinking skills	6	Sweetie dilemma				✓	✓	✓								✓				
Using and applying thinking skills	6	Money, money, money!															✓			
Using and applying thinking skills	6	What's my angle?															✓		✓	

Thinking by Numbers 4 and the 5–14 Guidelines

Thinking skill	Unit	Activity name	Problem solving and Enquiry	Information Handling	Range and Type of Numbers	Money	Add and Subtract	Multiply and Divide	Round Numbers	Fractions, Percentages and Ratio	Patterns and Sequences	Functions and Equations	Measure and Estimate	Time	Perimeter, Formulae and Scales	Shape, Position and Movement
Information processing	1	Aliens ahoy!	✓		✓											
		What do you need to know?	✓		✓	✓	✓	✓								
Reasoning	2	I can, I can't														✓
		Up the mountain			✓											
Enquiry	3	Who dunnit?	✓		✓					✓			✓			
		Mystery numbers	✓		✓		✓	✓								
Creative thinking	4	Tell me a story	✓											✓		
		Fraction time!	✓					✓		✓						
Evaluation	5	Good buy?	✓	✓		✓	✓									
		Best fit?	✓	✓	✓			✓								
Using and applying thinking skills	6	Sweetie dilemma	✓		✓								✓			
		Money, money, money!	✓		✓	✓	✓									
		What's my angle?	✓													✓